Biomechan

S0-AFV-610

CONCEPTS IN KINESIOLOGY

RICHARD GROVES, Ed. D.

Division of Physical Education
Central Connecticut State College

DAVID N. CAMAIONE, Ph. D.

Division of Physical Education
Central Connecticut State College

1975

W. B. SAUNDERS COMPANY • PHILADELPHIA • LONDON • TORONTO

W. B. Saunders Company: West Washington Square
Philadelphia, Pa. 19105

12 Dyott Street
London WC1A, 1DB

833 Oxford Street
Toronto, Ontario M8Z 5T9, Canada

Concepts in Kinesiology   ISBN   0-7216-4319-1

Last digit is the print number: 9   8   7   6   5   4   3   2   1

PREFACE

This text is designed to help undergraduate physical education majors increase their understanding of basic scientific information concerning human movement, by utilizing the conceptual approach.

In recent years the conceptual approach to learning has been emphasized. Our classroom teaching experience in undergraduate kinesiology permitted us to develop pertinent concepts for this subject matter. Each concept consists of three parts — (1) INFORMATION relevant to the concept is presented to introduce basic factual material; (2) a RATIONALE which explains the concept is presented; and (3) ACTIVITIES are provided for students to complete in order to reinforce understanding of the concept.

Mastery of these concepts should insure that the student has a basic knowledge of the subject matter of kinesiology. Obviously, the total knowledge of this broad field is not covered. To do so would defeat the purpose of this concise text. We are aware that the selection of the material and the way in which it is presented are subjective.

The material is presented in three main sections — Applied Anatomy, The Production of Motion, and Application.

Section One: Applied Anatomy, includes concepts concerning the PLANES AND AXES of the human body; the MUSCLES, which produce motion; the JOINTS, which permit the body to move; and KINESTHESIS, which assists in governing and modifying the production of motion.

Section Two: The Production of Motion, traces the generation of movement in the human body. FORCE acts upon LEVERS in order to develop TORQUE, which results in MOTION, a component of MOMENTUM. Motion is explained in terms of NEWTON'S LAWS and how these laws influence the CENTER OF GRAVITY and may cause problems in STABILITY.

Section Three: Application, provides for practical use of knowledge introduced in the first two sections. Included in this part is an area on FRICTION, in the absence of which motion cannot occur and an area on FOLLOW-THROUGH, an aid to efficient motion.

The objective is for students to apply knowledge gained from lectures, laboratory work, and textbook readings. Listed below are the bibliographical entries for ten popular kinesiology texts.

1. Barnham, J., and Wooten, E.: *Structural Kinesiology*. New York: The Macmillan Co., 1973.
2. Broer, M.: *Efficiency of Human Movement*. Philadelphia: W. B. Saunders Co., 1973.

3. Bunn, J. W.: *Scientific Principles of Coaching.* Englewood Cliffs, N.J.: Prentice-Hall, 1972.

4. Cooper, J., and Glassow, R.: *Kinesiology.* St. Louis: The C. V. Mosby Co., 1972.

5. Hay, J. G. *The Biomechanics of Sports Techniques.* Englewood Cliffs, N.J.: Prentice-Hall, 1973.

6. Jensen, C., and Schultz, G. *Applied Kinesiology.* New York: McGraw-Hill, 1970.

7. Logan, G., and McKinney, W.: *Kinesiology.* Dubuque: W. C. Brown, 1970.

8. Rasch, P., and Burke, R.: *Kinesiology and Applied Anatomy.* Philadelphia: Lea and Febiger, 1971.

9. Scott, M.: *Analysis of Human Motion.* New York: Appleton-Century-Crofts, 1963.

10. Wells, K.: *Kinesiology.* Philadelphia: W. B. Saunders Co., 1971.

We are indebted to our students, who served as subjects when this text was field tested. Special thanks is given to our good friend, J. Joseph Arnone, whose assistance on certain laws and principles of physics was invaluable.

RICHARD GROVES
DAVID N. CAMAIONE

CONTENTS

THE PRODUCTION OF MOTION

Section Three

APPLICATION

SECTION ONE

APPLIED ANATOMY

PLANES AND AXES

CONCEPT 1: PLANES AND AXES

THREE PLANES PASS THROUGH THE HUMAN BODY

INFORMATION:

1. A *plane*, in geometry, is a level and flat surface which is often imaginary.
2. Three planes of motion pass through the human body:
    a. *Sagittal plane* (anteroposterior): Passes through the body from front to back, dividing the body into left and right portions.
    b. *Frontal plane* (coronal): Passes through the body from left to right, dividing the body into anterior and posterior portions.
    c. *Horizontal plane* (transverse): Passes through the body in a line parallel to the floor and divides the body into superior and inferior portions.
3. A *cardinal plane* (primary) divides the body into equal portions. The horizontal cardinal plane, for example, divides the body into superior and inferior portions of equal size.
4. The three planes passing through the human body lie at right angles (are perpendicular) to each other.
5. Where the three cardinal planes intersect one another lies the *center of gravity* of the body.

RATIONALE:

Three planes pass through the human body. Human movements are typically described in terms of the plane in which they occur. Axes of motion are described according to the two planes which they occupy. Flexion of the glenohumeral joint may be defined as a forward movement in the sagittal plane around an axis which occupies the frontal and horizontal planes.

A plane may pass through the body at any point and may divide the body into unequal segments; e.g., the horizontal plane may pass through the body at the ankles.

ACTIVITIES:

1. Complete the following table by supplying the plane of motion in which the action occurs.

Action	Plane
Softball pitch	_____
Sidearm throw	_____

Jumping jack exercise   _____

Flutter kick in swimming   _____

Pirouette   _____

2. In the drawing below, label the three planes which pass through the body.

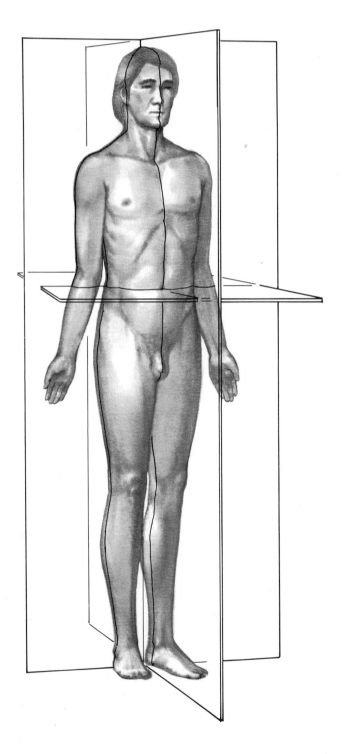

CONCEPT 2: PLANES AND AXES

HUMAN MOTION IS DESCRIBED FROM THE ANATOMICAL POSITION

INFORMATION:

The *anatomical position* is one in which the subject assumes the position of military attention with the palms facing forward.

RATIONALE:

Elbow flexion may occur in different planes. If the arm hangs naturally, elbow flexion occurs in the sagittal plane. If the arms are parallel to the floor with the palms facing upward, it occurs in the frontal plane. When the arms are parallel to the floor but with the palms facing forward, elbow flexion occurs in the horizontal plane.

It is evident that there must be a standardized reference position from which movements occurring at joints can be described. This fundamental frame of reference is the anatomical position.

ACTIVITIES:

Complete the following table by listing the plane in which the motion occurs. In all cases the person is in the anatomical position.

Movement	Plane
Wrist extension	Sagittal
Ulnar deviation	
Hip rotation	
Abduction of leg	
Plantar flexion	
Inversion of foot	
Supination of forearm	

Anterior pelvic tilt   _____

Lateral pelvic tilt   _____

Hyperextension of trunk   _____

CONCEPT 3: PLANES AND AXES

AN AXIS OF MOTION OCCUPIES TWO PLANES

INFORMATION:

1. An *axis* is a fixed point about which *angular motion* occurs.
2. A pendulum is an example of an object exhibiting angular motion. One end of the pendulum serves as an axis while the distal end describes an arc.
3. Nearly all the movements occurring at human body joints are angular motion.

RATIONALE:

An axis is the intersection of two planes. The motion occurring around the axis occurs in the third plane.

Flexion and extension of the elbow are angular movements. As described from the anatomical position, they occur in the sagittal plane around an axis of motion that occupies the frontal and horizontal planes.

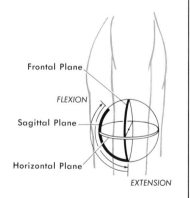

Ulnar deviation and radial deviation occur at the wrist and are movements in the frontal plane. They occur around an axis that occupies the sagittal and horizontal planes.

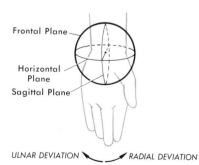

ACTIVITIES

1. Label the planes occupied by the axes of motion for the following movements.

   a. Flexion and extension of the glenohumeral joint.

   _____

   _____

   b. Abduction and adduction of the glenohumeral joint.

   _____

   _____

   c. Medial and lateral rotation of the glenohumeral joint.

   _____

   _____

2. Complete the following table.

Movement	Plane in Which Movement Occurs	Planes Occupied by Axis of Motion
Plantar flexion	Sagittal	Horizontal-Frontal
Neck flexion		
Supination		
Knee flexion		
Hip extension		
Posterior tilt (pelvis)		
Trunk extension		
Scapula adduction		
Femur rotation		
Trunk rotation		

MUSCLES

CONCEPT 4: The functioning of a motor unit aids in our understanding of nerve-muscle activity.

CONCEPT 5: Muscles are subject to isometric and isotonic contractions.

CONCEPT 6: Isotonic muscle contractions may be concentric or eccentric.

CONCEPT 7: Arrangement of muscle fibers into fusiform or pennate designs determines muscle action.

CONCEPT 8: Muscles which pass a joint act at that joint. There are single-joint, two-joint, and multi-joint muscles.

CONCEPT 9: Muscle fibers are classified into two general physiological types: pale and red.

CONCEPT 10: There exists an inverse relationship between mechanical and physiological advantages of muscle.

CONCEPT 11: Muscles may act as "spurt" or "shunt" muscles.

CONCEPT 12: A muscle may play one of many roles during joint movement.

CONCEPT 13: Human skeletal muscles often play a stabilizing role.

CONCEPT 14: Muscles may play the roles of true synergist and helping synergist.

CONCEPT 15: The line of pull of a muscle is dependent upon the position of its attachments.

CONCEPT 16: Muscles may pull from either direction, a concept referred to as functional reversibility.

CONCEPT 17: The brachialis muscle is called the "true flexor of the elbow."

CONCEPT 18: An uneven pull in bilateral muscles may force the vertebral column out of alignment, causing displacement of body parts.

CONCEPT 19: Faulty alignment of one body segment often forces neighboring sections out of alignment.

CONCEPT 4: MUSCLES

THE FUNCTIONING OF A MOTOR UNIT AIDS IN OUR UNDERSTANDING OF NERVE-MUSCLE ACTIVITY

INFORMATION:

1. A *motor unit* is defined as a neuron and the muscle fibers it innervates. Depending upon the type of muscle, a ratio of 1:150 is a normal figure.
2. Where fine coordinated activity occurs, the ratio is increased, i.e., 1:10; whereas in gross motor activity, the ratio may decrease to 1:200. One may recall that the degree of nerve tissue of the motor cortex is abundant for the hand and face.
3. Motor units lie close to one another and often interdigitation among muscle fibers occurs.
4. The motor unit functions under the principle of the "all or none law"; that is, when activated, all muscle fibers in the unit contract maximally or not at all.

RATIONALE:

When one moves a given load (resistance), sufficent motor units have "turned-on." If the load is greater, increased motor units come into play, a concept referred to as recruitment.

"Muscle tone" simply implies that a muscle possesses a degree of muscle tension. This tension is developed as a result of motor unit activity. For example, to prevent fatigue, some working units "turn-off" while idle units "turn-on," thus maintaining a constant state of partial contraction.

11

ACTIVITIES:

1. Describe the following relationship.

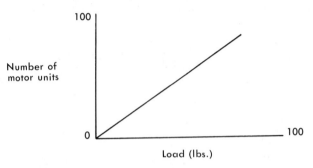

Answer:

CONCEPT 5: MUSCLES

MUSCLES ARE SUBJECT TO ISOMETRIC AND ISOTONIC CONTRACTIONS

INFORMATION:

Isometric contraction involves no overt change in the length of a muscle; whereas *isotonic contraction* does involve overt change in the length of the muscle.

RATIONALE:

Bones move principally because muscles shorten and pull on the bone to which they attach, overcoming the resistance. This type of contraction is termed isotonic.

In some instances a muscle may attempt to shorten but cannot do so because it cannot move a resistance. An example would be a person standing in a doorway attempting to push the sides of the doorway apart. This type of contraction is termed isometric.

During isometric contraction no resistance is moved because the muscle does not shorten. However, it is evident that the muscle is working (contracting) because heat is produced and the temperature (internal) of the muscle rises.

ACTIVITIES:

1. How would you counter the physicists' argument that no work is done during isometric contraction since no resistance is moved? (W = Fd) (Note: Heat is a by-product of work).

2. Circle the number of the following statements which depict isometric contractions and underline those which depict isotonic contractions.
    1. Attempting to pull a tank.
    2. Shooting free throws.
    3. Climbing a rope.

4. Pushing outward on a doorway.
5. Propelling a shot put.
6. Lifting a prize steer.
7. Biting on a bullet.
8. Executing a pull-up.
9. Shovelling snow.
10. Pulling at the ends of a towel.

CONCEPT 6: MUSCLES

ISOTONIC MUSCLE CONTRACTIONS MAY BE CONCENTRIC OR ECCENTRIC

INFORMATION:

1. Isotonic contraction involves a change in length of a muscle with the muscle either lengthening or shortening.
2. When a muscle shortens from its resting length, the isotonic contraction is termed *concentric*.
3. When a previously contracted muscle lengthens, the isotonic contraction is termed *eccentric*.

RATIONALE:

Eccentric contraction involves the gradual lengthening, in a controlled manner, of a previously contracted muscle. A major purpose of eccentric contraction is to gradually lower the body, or body part, in a controlled manner against the pull of gravity.

A performer arrives at the top of a push-up by means of concentric isotonic contraction of the elbow extensors and scapular abductors. As he lowers his body to the floor, he does not allow gravity to exert its full effect, or injury might result if the torso plummets downward. What the performer does is to allow his previously contracted elbow extensors and scapula abductors to gradually lengthen (eccentric isotonic contraction) in order to lower his torso to the floor in a controlled manner.

A major point in isotonic muscle contraction is that the muscles that raise the resistance via concentric contraction also lower the resistance via eccentric contraction.

ACTIVITIES:

Identify the following examples as the result of either *concentric* or *eccentric* isotonic contraction.

Upward movement in a chin-up.   _____

Downward portion of chin-up.   _____

Elbow flexion (forearm curl).   _____

15

Trunk flexion while standing.   _____

Lowering recovery leg in walking.   _____

Sitting down on a chair.   _____

Downward movement in sit-up.   _____

Lowering barbell from forearm curl.   _____

CONCEPT 7: MUSCLES

ARRANGEMENT OF MUSCLE FIBERS INTO FUSIFORM OR PENNATE DESIGNS DETERMINES MUSCLE ACTION

INFORMATION:

1. *Fusiform* muscle fibers are those whose fascicles consist of parallel fibers running the length of the muscle.
2. *Pennate* muscle fibers are those which have fascicles running obliquely to a central tendon. They give the appearance of a feather.
3. *Fusiform* fibers are generally weak but shorten over long distances, giving the advantage of speed at the expense of strength.
4. *Pennate* muscle fibers are generally stronger muscles which shorten over shorter distances but with greater force at the expense of speed.
5. There are several types of pennate structures: *unipennate, bipennate,* and *multipennate.*

RATIONALE:

The human body is designed for speed and range of motion. Most of our muscles are strategically placed to bring about greater force of contraction to overcome the inherent weakness of third-class levers.

The large muscle groups in the lower extremities are predominantly pennate arrangements, since these are used for such powerful acts as jumping, sprinting, and climbing.

ACTIVITIES:

1. Draw a fusiform, a unipennate, a bipennate, and a multipennate muscle arrangement.

           Fusiform   *Unipennate*

Bipennate   *Multipennate*

2. Give the type of fiber arrangement (fusiform, bipennate, etc.) for each of the following muscles. (See Preface.)

Muscle	*Fiber Arrangement*	*Advantage*
Biceps brachii	_____	_____
Gastrocnemius	_____	_____
Deltoid	_____	_____
Quadriceps femoris	_____	_____
Brachioradialis	_____	_____
Triceps brachii	_____	_____

CONCEPT 8: MUSCLES

MUSCLES WHICH PASS A JOINT ACT AT THAT JOINT. THERE ARE SINGLE-JOINT, TWO-JOINT, AND MULTI-JOINT MUSCLES

INFORMATION:

1. A single-joint muscle is one which acts only at one joint. The brachialis muscle passes only the elbow joint; thus, its sole job is to flex the forearm.
2. A two-joint muscle is one which acts at two joints. The biceps brachii muscle passes the glenohumeral and elbow joints and acts to flex the arm at the shoulder and the forearm at the elbow.
3. A multi-joint muscle is one which acts at several joints. The flexor digitorum profundus muscle passes the elbow, wrist, several carpal, and finger joints. As a consequence, it can aid in the action of the many bony segments it passes.

RATIONALE:

One moves as a result of muscle action, not of single muscle involvement but of muscle group action. Research has indicated that if several single-joint muscles were used for given joint action, considerably more energy would be needed than if a lesser number of two-joint or multi-joint muscles were utilized.

Further evidence has shown that two-joint muscles do not lose their tension level. While lengthening at one joint, tension is increased; however, tension is decreased while shortening at the other joint.

ACTIVITIES:

1. For each of the following, find a pair of antagonistic muscles about the same joint(s).

Single-joint muscle pair _____
Two-joint muscle pair _____
Multi-joint muscle pair _____

2. State the actions and the joints involved for each of the following muscles.

Actions and Joints

Triceps brachii _____

Biceps femoris _____

Extensor digitorum communis _____

Gastrocnemius _____

Brachioradialis _____

CONCEPT 9: MUSCLES

MUSCLE FIBERS ARE CLASSIFIED INTO TWO GENERAL PHYSIOLOGICAL TYPES: PALE AND RED

INFORMATION:

1. *Myoglobin,* a substance having a high affinity for oxygen, is the determining factor in whether a muscle is classified pale or dark.
2. *Dark* (red) *muscle* fiber has greater amounts of myoglobin, more mitochondria, and utilizes the *oxidative processes* for energy supply.
3. *Pale* (white) *muscle* fiber has lesser amounts of myoglobin, less mitochondria, and utilizes the *glycolytic* sequence for energy supply.
4. The human musculature has characteristically mixed fibers within a muscle. Within lower animal life one might find a muscle predominantly dark or pale.

RATIONALE:

Dark (red) muscle fibers have the physiologic advantage of sustaining contractions over longer periods of time. Consequently, these muscle fibers are found in our posture muscles, those which are under constant stress from the force of gravity. Activities such as sitting, standing, and walking use dark muscle predominantly. Their contractions are slower and more sustained, but powerful. Any of our aerobic exercises would place great demand on these muscle fibers.

Pale (white) muscle fibers have the capacity to work quickly and derive their energy from *anaerobic metabolism.* Explosive or short-duration activities would place great demand upon these fiber types. Rapid ballistic actions, such as throwing, would call upon pale fibers.

ACTIVITIES:

1. List ten major muscles and indicate whether they would be classified pale, dark, or mixed. (See Preface.)

	Muscle	*Fiber Type*	*Type of Contraction*
1.	Soleus	Dark	Sustaining contraction
2.			
3.			
4.			
5.			
6.			
7.			
8.			
9.			
10.			

2. From the field of physical education and athletics list five activities which would place particular demand upon pale (white) muscles and five activities for dark (red) muscles.

Pale Muscle Activities	*Dark Muscle Activities*
1.	1.
2.	2.
3.	3.
4.	4.
5.	5.

CONCEPT 10: MUSCLES

THERE EXISTS AN INVERSE RELATIONSHIP BETWEEN THE MECHANICAL AND PHYSIOLOGICAL ADVANTAGES OF MUSCLE

INFORMATION:

1. *Mechanical advantage* refers to the amount of resistance overcome in ratio to the amount of effort expended.
2. The mechanical advantage of a contracting muscle is greatest when the *angle of pull* of that muscle is 90 degrees.
3. The *angle of pull* of a muscle is the angle formed between the plane of the bone and the line of pull of a contracting muscle.
4. The *physiological advantage* of muscle refers to the ability of a muscle to shorten.
5. A muscle possesses its greatest physiological advantage when at, or stretched beyond, its *resting length.*

RATIONALE:

If a ten pound weight is lifted one foot when ten foot-pounds of muscular effort are expended, the mechanical advantage is unity (1.00).

A performer hangs from a chin-up bar by his hands with the arms straight. He wishes to perform a chin-up. The angles of pull of his elbow flexors are near zero, resulting in poor mechanical advantages for these muscles. However, since the muscles are stretched beyond resting lengths, they are in a position of physiological advantage. As the performer elevates his body, the physiological advantage of these muscles is decreased, whereas the angles of pull of the elbow flexors increased toward 90 degrees. This demonstrates the inverse ratio of physiological efficiency and mechanical efficiency in the chin-up exercise.

As the angle of pull deviates from 90 degrees, the mechanical advantage decreases. At zero degrees of muscle pull, the mechanical advantage of the muscle is zero; however, the physiological advantage is greatest at this angle.

ACTIVITIES:

Anser the following questions concerning a performer who executes a deep knee bend.

23

1. What type of muscle contraction allowed the performer to assume the deep knee bend? What muscle groups were involved?
   a.
   b.
2. What type of muscle contraction allowed the performer to return to the anatomical position? What muscle groups were involved?
   a.
   b.
3. What muscles are placed on stretch while in the deep knee bend position?

4. Which muscle advantage (mechanical or physiological) is greater while in the deep knee bend position?

5. As the legs extend, what change occurs in the angle of pull of the working muscles? What is the effect on the mechanical advantage of these muscles? What is the effect on the physiological advantage of these muscles?
   a.
   b.
   c.
6. Expain the relationship which exists between the physiological advantage and the mechanical advantage of muscle.

CONCEPT 11: MUSCLES

MUSCLES MAY ACT AS SPURT OR SHUNT MUSCLES

INFORMATION:

1. A *spurt muscle* has its upper attachment at a distance from the joint upon which it acts and its lower attachment closer to that joint. Example: biceps at the elbow.
2. A *shunt muscle* has its upper attachment nearer the joint upon which it acts than is true of its lower attachment. Example: brachioradialis at the elbow.

RATIONALE:

One of the factors that determine the amount of force a contracting muscle exerts to move a bone is the distance from the attachment of that muscle to the joint. The greater this distance, the more effective the muscle in moving the bone.

"Spurt" muscles have their lower attachments at a point close to the joint upon which they act and are more effective in producing rapid movement against relatively small resistances.

"Shunt" muscles have their lower attachments at a point some distance from the joint upon which they act. Most of their force is directed along the bone and is more effective in stabilizing the bones which articulate to form the joint. "Shunt" muscles also serve as assistant movers when there is considerable resistance to overcome. The role of the brachioradialis in elbow flexion illustrates this assistant mover function.

ACTIVITIES:

Classify each of the following muscles as a spurt or a shunt muscle. Consult your textbook to identify the attachments of the muscles in question.

Muscles	*Category*
Triceps (elbow action)	_____
Triceps (glenohumeral action)	_____
Sternocleidomastoideus (head)	_____
Brachioradialis	_____

Muscles	Category
Hamstrings (for hip extension)	_____
Hamstrings (for knee flexion)	_____
Biceps (for shoulder flexion)	_____
Biceps (for elbow flexion)	_____

CONCEPT 12: MUSCLES

A MUSCLE MAY PLAY ONE OF MANY ROLES DURING JOINT MOVEMENT

INFORMATION:

1. *Prime mover*: A muscle is a prime mover (agonist) when it produces most of the force which moves a bone. There may be more than one prime mover involved in a joint movement. Most muscles which span two joints are prime movers of the distal joint spanned. Example: hamstrings during knee flexion.
2. *Assistant mover*: A muscle is an assistant mover when it aids a prime mover in overcoming considerable resistance. Most two-joint muscles are assistant movers of the proximal joint spanned. Example: biceps in flexion of glenohumeral joint.
3. *Antagonist*: A muscle is an antagonist when its action opposes the movement occurring at a joint. Example: biceps during elbow extension.
4. *Stabilizer*: A muscle is a stabilizer when it fixes one bony segment so that a movement can occur at a bone articulating at that bony segment. Example: quadratus lumborum stabilizes left hip as the left leg swings forward when running.
5. *Helping synergist*: Two muscles are helping synergists when they cancel each other's undesired movement, thereby allowing each other's desired movement to occur. Note: when a muscle contracts, it produces all the movements which nature designed it to produce. Some mechanism must exist to cancel out the undesired movements.
6. *True synergist*: A muscle is a true synergist when its movements cancel the undesired movement of a prime mover. Example: pronator quadratus cancels the tendency of biceps to supinate the forearm as the biceps flexes the forearm.

RATIONALE:

A muscle may play any one of six roles during a single-joint movement. However, one muscle cannot play more than one role simultaneously during any single movement.

ACTIVITIES:

Complete the following table by stating the role and action of each of the muscles.

Action	Muscle	Role
Walking	Left quadratus lumborum	Stabilizing left hip
Forearm curl	Biceps	_____
Crawl stroke (shoulder)	Triceps	_____
Bilateral leg lift	Rectus abdominis	_____
Supination of forearm	Triceps	_____
Batting softball (elbow)	Triceps	_____
Batting softball (elbow)	Biceps	_____
Golf drive	Oblique abdominals	_____

CONCEPT 13: MUSCLES

HUMAN SKELETAL MUSCLES OFTEN PLAY A STABILIZING ROLE

INFORMATION:

A muscle serves as a stabilizer when it fixes a bony segment so that motion may occur at a bone which articulates at that fixed segment. (See Concept 12.)

RATIONALE:

In performing bilateral leg lifts, a subject lies in the supine position and raises (flexes) both femurs simultaneously. The knees remain extended.

The femurs insert into the acetabula of the pelvis. When the femurs are flexed, the hip flexor muscles attempt to pull the pelvis into a position of anterior tilt. Some muscle or muscle group must contract and fix the pelvis, preventing the pelvis from moving into the undesired position of anterior tilt.

The abdominal muscles, chiefly rectus abdominis, contract isometrically and stabilize the pelvis from tilting anteriorly. A person unaccustomed to bilateral leg lifts may experience postexercise soreness in the abdominal muscles. The abdominals do not flex the femurs. It is the stabilizing effort of the abdominals which causes the soreness.

ACTIVITIES:

Complete the following table by listing the stabilizing muscles. (Consider the movement that gravity would attempt to produce in the stabilized segment.)

Action	Segment Stabilized	Movement Produced by Gravity	Stabilizing Muscle(s)
Chin-up	Pelvis	Anterior tilt	Rectus abdominis
Elbow flexion	Scapula		

Action	Segment Stabilized	Movement Produced by Gravity	Stabilizing Muscle(s)
Forearm curl	Wrist	_____	_____
Reverse curl	Wrist	_____	_____
Football punt	Pelvis	_____	_____
Push-up	Vertebral column	_____	_____

CONCEPT 14: MUSCLES

MUSCLES MAY PLAY THE ROLES OF TRUE SYNERGIST AND HELPING SYNERGIST

INFORMATION:

1. When a muscle contracts, it seeks to produce all the joint movements which nature designed it to produce.
2. *Helping synergists* prohibit one another's undesired movements in order to permit each other's desired movements to occur. Each synergistic muscle produces the desired movement. (See Concept 12.)
3. A *true synergist* does not participate in producing the desired movement. It merely prohibits the undesired movement of the prime movers. (See Concept 12.)

RATIONALE:

Muscles are nonselective regarding which of their possible movements are produced. When a muscle contracts, it attempts to cause all the movements which it is designed to produce at that joint. Some other muscle acting upon that joint must prohibit the undesired movements.

Two mechanisms exist by which undesired movements may be prohibited. The first is called helping synergy. Biceps femoris flexes the knee and rotates it laterally, while the medial hamstrings flex the knee and rotate it medially. When knee flexion alone is the desired outcome, these synergists prohibit each other's undesired movement (rotation), and each serves as a prime mover in producing the desired movement (flexion).

The second mechanism is true synergy. The rectus femoris seeks to extend the knee and flex the thigh. The hamstrings extend the thigh. When knee extension alone is desired, the hamstrings contract to prevent the undesired movement of the rectus femoris (flexion of the thigh). Note that only one of the synergists serves as a prime mover in true synergy.

ACTIVITIES:

1. Helping synergy: The trunk flexors cause the vertebral column to rotate. The trunk extensors also cause the vertebral column to rotate. When

31

swinging a softball bat, trunk rotation is the desired movement. Complete the following table.

Desired Outcome — Trunk Rotation

Muscle Group	Desired Movement	Undesired Movement
Trunk flexors	_____	_____
Trunk extensors	_____	_____
Outcome	_____	

2. True synergy: The biceps seeks to supinate and flex the forearm. The triceps extends the forearm at the elbow. When throwing a curve ball, supination is the desired movement. Complete the following table.

Desired Outcome — Forearm Supination

Muscle	Desired Movement	Undesired Movement
Biceps	_____	_____
Triceps	_____	
Outcome	_____	

CONCEPT 15: MUSCLES

THE LINE OF PULL OF A MUSCLE IS DEPENDENT UPON THE POSITION OF ITS ATTACHMENTS

INFORMATION:

1. The functional pulling axis or *line of pull* of a muscle can be ascertained by locating its attachments.
2. Muscles which pass the anterior aspect of the elbow joint will serve as flexors; muscles which lie in the medial compartment of the thigh are adductors.
3. However, most muscles are attached to the upper (proximal) bone and pull to move the lower (distal) bone.

RATIONALE:

Memorizing the many muscle attachments gives one a greater understanding of muscle function. Being able to visualize where muscles arise and where they go as they pass a particular joint(s) gives a clearer picture of muscle group function.

The teaching of skill and/or specific exercises is completed more easily when the physical educator and coach possess suffcient knowledge relative to muscle position. Often improper teaching and coaching techniques are employed because valuable knowledge of anatomical structure is neglected.

ACTIVITIES:

Place a check mark in the column which indicates the proper action for each of the muscles listed.

Location of Muscle	Flexion	Extension	Adduction	Abduction
Muscle spanning elbow joint anteriorly	_____	_____	_____	_____
Muscle spanning femoral region medially	_____	_____	_____	_____

Location of Muscle	Flexion	Extension	Adduction	Abduction
Muscle spanning shoulder joint laterally	_____	_____	_____	_____
Muscle spanning ankle anteriorly	_____	_____	_____	_____

CONCEPT 16: MUSCLES

MUSCLES MAY PULL FROM EITHER DIRECTION, A CONCEPT REFERRED TO AS FUNCTIONAL REVERSIBILITY

INFORMATION:

1. The *origin* (upper attachment) of a muscle is referred to as the fixed point and is toward the axial skeleton.
2. The *insertion* (lower attachment) of a muscle is referred to as the moving point and is away from the axial skeleton.

RATIONALE:

When studying the anatomy of muscles and their attachments, memorization of origins and insertions is necessary. Unfortunately, such learning leads us to believe that the origins are always fixed points, while the insertions are always the moving points.

This reasoning does not always hold true. In some motor acts the roles are reversed; the origin becomes the moving point, and the insertion becomes the fixed (stable) point. For example, the sternocleidomastoid muscle arises from the sternum, and runs superiorly and laterally to insert on the mastoid process of the temporal bone. Its primary function is rotation of the head. However, if the head becomes fixed, the muscle pulls upon its lower attachment (origin), causing it to move. This action occurs when the individual is breathing heavily and utilizes this muscle as an assistant mover during inhalation.

ACTIVITIES:

If the activity calls for moving the lower attachment toward the upper one, place a check in that column. If the upper attachment is moving toward the lower, place a check in that column.

Activity	L toward U	U toward L
Forearm curl (biceps)	_____	_____
Sit-up (rectus abdominis)	_____	_____

Activity	L toward U	U toward L
Pull-up (biceps)		
Leg raises (iliopsoas)		
Neck flexion (scaleni)		
Forced inspiration (scaleni)		
Bench press (pectoralis major)		
Shoulder adduction (middle trapezius)		

CONCEPT 17: MUSCLES

THE BRACHIALIS MUSCLE IS CALLED THE TRUE FLEXOR OF THE ELBOW

INFORMATION:

1. The brachialis runs from the lower half of the anterior humerus to the coronoid process of the ulna. It flexes the forearm.
2. The biceps brachii runs from the scapula to the tuberosity of the radius. It seeks to flex and supinate the forearm.
3. The brachioradialis runs from the lower third of the humerus to the distal end of the radius. It flexes, semipronates and semisupinates the forearm.

RATIONALE:

For the following reasons, the brachialis muscle is termed the *true flexor of the elbow.*

The biceps has a second duty of providing supination, so only when the forearm is supinated can the biceps effectively flex the elbow.

The biceps and the brachioradialis attach upon the radius, thus spanning the elbow diagonally. A poor line of pull exists for elbow flexion.

The brachioradialis has a secondary function of semipronation and semisupination.

The brachioradialis is a shunt muscle, and is therefore an assistant mover rather than a prime mover for elbow flexion. (See Concept 11.)

The brachialis is the only flexor which spans the two bones, humerus and ulna, which articulate to form the elbow joint. This muscle has a better line of pull for elbow flexion.

The brachialis has only one function—flexion of the elbow.

ACTIVITIES:

Answer the following questions.
1. Which elbow flexors have secondary functions?

2. Which elbow flexors have poor lines of pull for flexion?

3. What muscle has no other role except elbow flexion?

4. What muscle has the best line of pull for elbow flexion?

5. Which elbow flexor can make the greatest contribution to elbow flexion?

CONCEPT 18: MUSCLES

AN UNEVEN PULL IN BILATERAL MUSCLES MAY FORCE THE VERTEBRAL COLUMN OUT OF ALIGNMENT, CAUSING DISPLACEMENT OF BODY PARTS

INFORMATION:

1. There are bilateral muscles attached to either side of the vertebral column. Example: left and right quadratus lumborum.
2. An uneven pull in bilateral muscles may pull the vertebral column out of alignment.
3. An uneven pull in paired antagonists also may force the vertebral column out of alignment. Example: iliocostalis lumborum and psoas major.

RATIONALE:

When one paired muscle attached to the vertebral column becomes stronger than its counterpart, the vertebral column may be pulled out of its normal alignment. Should the right intertransversarii muscles become stronger than the identical muscles on the left side, the result, over a period of time, could be a convexity to the right of the lower vertebral column. The same malformation could occur if the left intertransversarii muscles were rendered invalid through injury or disease.

A similar problem occurs if a muscle attaching to the anterior portion of the vertebral column becomes stronger than its antagonist at the rear of the column. For example, if the two sternocleidomastoids should become stronger than the two splenius cervicis muscles, the result would be a flattening of the normal curve of the cervical vertebrae. The same abnormality would appear if the two splenius cervicis muscles were rendered invalid through injury or disease.

ACTIVITIES:

1. The oblique fibers of the two quadratus lumborum muscles run from the iliac crest to the transverse processes of the lumbar vertebrae. Let us

39

assume that the nerves innervating the right muscle are affected by disease.
   a. What will be the effect on the lumbar spine?
   b. Why?

2. The splenus capitus muscles become stronger than, and overpower, the scaleni muscles.
   a. What will be the effect on the cervical spine?
   b. Why?

3. The psoas major muscles become stronger than the iliocostalis lumborum muscles.
   a. What will be the effect upon the lumbar spine?

   b. Why should coaches not require an excessive number of "sit-up" calisthenics?

CONCEPT 19: MUSCLES

FAULTY ALIGNMENT OF ONE BODY SEGMENT OFTEN FORCES NEIGHBORING SEGMENTS OUT OF ALIGNMENT

INFORMATION:

1. The body segments are joined at articulations.
2. The body may be compared to a chain. When one link of a strong chain is forced out of alignment, neighboring links are also affected.

RATIONALE:

If muscular imbalance causes the lumbar spine to be pulled out of alignment, the pelvis, femurs, and even the knees may become displaced. Should any of these four segments become misaligned, the other three segments are often adversely affected. This phenomenon is referred to as *adaptation of stress.*

For example, anterior tilt of the pelvis may result in an increased curvature of the lumbar spine, abnormal flexion of the acetabula of the pelvis over the femurs, and hyperextended knees.

ACTIVITIES:

Complete the following chart. The spaces which are marked by asterisks represent the segments originally displaced. Fill in the effects of the original displacement on the other body segments.

Vertebral Column	Pelvis	Femurs in Acetabula	Knees
			Hyperextended*

41

| | | Femurs in | |
Vertebral Column	Pelvis	Acetabula	Knees
Left lateral flexion*			(none)
	Posterior tilt*		
		Adduction(right femur)*	(none)

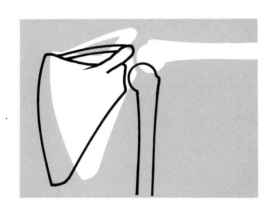

JOINTS

CONCEPT 20: Kinesiologists classify joints according to the degree of movement they possess.

CONCEPT 21: Only three basic movements occur in the human body — bending, stretching, and twisting.

CONCEPT 22: An inverse relationship exists between mobility and stability in human joints.

CONCEPT 23: Medial and lateral rotation of the glenohumeral joint are analogous to pronation and supination at the radio-ulnar joints.

CONCEPT 24: Movements at the glenohumeral joint are accompanied by accommodating movements at the scapula and clavicle.

CONCEPT 20: JOINTS

KINESIOLOGISTS CLASSIFY JOINTS ACCORDING TO THE DEGREE OF MOVEMENT THEY POSSESS

INFORMATION:

1. Joints of the human body are classified into three major types—*synarthrodial, amphiarthrodial,* and *diarthrodial.*
2. *Synarthrodial joints* possess no articular cavity and are immovable, owing primarily to their structural unit. Sutures of the skull are an example.
3. *Amphiarthrodial joints* also possess no articular cavity but are slightly moveable. The pubic symphysis is an example.
4. *Diarthrodial joints* possess an articular cavity and free movement. They have six subtypes and exist in abundance in the human body.

RATIONALE:

The human body is simply a series of connected blocks, rods, spheres, and the like, linked at points referred to as articulations (joints). Students of human movement must possess a good understanding of joint structure and resulting freedom of movement.

Certain structural characteristics are specific to the joint type. Knowing these details aids in understanding the particular strengths and weaknesses a joint possesses. Physical educators are often asked to interpret the degree of movement as they teach sport skills. Structural limitations of a joint or group of joints dictate the style of movement pattern that is to be expected. The significance of joint movement becomes paramount in analyzing total human movement.

ACTIVITIES:

Below is a list of major joints of the body; give the general classification—synarthrodial, amphiarthrodial, or diarthroidial.

Joint	*Classification*
Knee	Diarthrodial
Glenohumeral	

45

Joint	*Classification*
Hip	_____
Vertebral bodies	_____
Lumbosacral	_____
Ankle	_____
Acromioclavicular	_____
Wrist	_____
Atlantoaxial	_____
Coracoclavicular	_____

CONCEPT 21: JOINTS

ONLY THREE BASIC MOVEMENTS OCCUR IN THE HUMAN BODY — BENDING, STRETCHING, AND TWISTING

INFORMATION:

1. *Bending* occurs when the body or body part flexes and confines itself to less space.
2. *Stretching* occurs when the body or body part extends and occupies more space.
3. *Twisting* occurs when the body or body part rotates about its longitudinal axis. (Not to be confused with torque, since all these basic movements involve the concept of torque.)

RATIONALE:

Students of human movement are quick to realize that the movements of bending, stretching, and twisting combine to develop into fundamental movement patterns such as running, walking, jumping, throwing, and striking.

Proper motor skill execution depends primarily upon one's musculoskeletal limitations, although secondary factors like physiological efficiency, attitude, skill, and body awareness have powerful effects in coordinating the movements of bending, stretching, and twisting. Confining one's body parts to limited space or expanding these parts to take up space necessitates coordinated muscular effort if more advanced skills are to be executed.

Thus, the performance of a skillful forward somersault with a half twist to a back handspring demonstrates the combining effects of the three basic movements.

ACTIVITIES:

Classify the following skills as either bending, stretching, or twisting. (Answer in terms of the performer's being in the process of executing the skill.)

Skill	*Basic Movement*
Tuck forward roll	Bending
Cartwheel	_____
Pirouette	_____
Vertical jump	_____
Racer's start (swimming)	_____
Bench press	_____
Swan dive	_____

CONCEPT 22: JOINTS

AN INVERSE RELATIONSHIP EXISTS BETWEEN MOBILITY AND STABILITY IN HUMAN JOINTS

INFORMATION:

1. Some of the factors accounting for stability in human joints are the amount of ligamentous support, the amount of contact between the articulating bones, and the number and strength of the muscles which span the joint.
2. As the factors stated above increase, the stability of that joint increases, but its *mobility* decreases. As the factors stated above decrease, the stability of that joint decreases, but its mobility increases.

RATIONALE:

If a joint possesses stability, the amount of contact between the articulating bones, the amount of ligamentous support, and the number and strength of the muscles spanning the joint must all contribute to that stability. However, these factors limit the ability of the joint to move, thus decreasing its mobility.

On the other hand, if a joint has less surface contact between its articulating bones, limited ligamentous support, and a small number of muscles spanning it, that joint normally lacks stability. When these factors contribute little to joint stability, joint mobility is increased.

ACTIVITIES:

The hip and shoulder joints are two examples of enarthrodial joints in the human body. These two joints clearly illustrate the inverse relationship between mobility and stability. Answer the following questions:

1. Which joint has the stronger ligaments reinforcing it?
2. Which joint has the more powerful muscles spanning it?
3. Which joint has the greatest degree of contact between the articulating bones?

4. Which joint possesses the greatest stability? Why?
    a.
    b.
5. Which joint possesses the greatest mobility? Why?
    a.
    b.

CONCEPT 23: JOINTS

MEDIAL AND LATERAL ROTATION OF THE GLENOHUMERAL JOINT ARE ANALOGOUS TO PRONATION AND SUPINATION AT THE RADIOULNAR JOINTS

INFORMATION:

1. All human movements are described from the *anatomical position*. (See Concept 2.)
2. Supination and pronation occur at the radioulnar articulations. When supinated, the palms face forward; when pronated, the palms face rearward.
3. When the glenohumeral joints are laterally rotated, the palms of the hands face forward. The palms face rearward when the glenohumeral joints are medially rotated.

RATIONALE:

Here is a situation in which the final position of the hands can result from two sets of movements. When analyzing a motor skill, it becomes necessary to understand joint movements which produce the final hand position. For example, in throwing a curve ball pitch in baseball, the final hand position is one of supination, resulting from both supination of the forearm and lateral rotation of the glenohumeral joint.

ACTIVITIES:

Complete the following table.

Movement	Joint Involved	Agonist Muscles
Pronation		
Medial rotation		
Supination		
Lateral rotation		

CONCEPT 24: JOINTS

MOVEMENTS AT THE GLENOHUMERAL JOINT ARE ACCOMPANIED BY ACCOMMODATING MOVEMENTS AT THE SCAPULA AND CLAVICLE

INFORMATION:

1. Each *pectoral girdle* consists of a scapula, clavicle, humerus, and the involved articulations. When one of these bones moves, the other two make accommodating movements.
2. Most of the movements in the pectoral girdle are initiated by the humerus or scapula. The clavicle is not capable of independent movement.

RATIONALE:

The pectoral girdle may be compared to a three-link chain. When one of the links moves, the other two must make accommodating movements. Otherwise, the primary movement would be inhibited.

ACTIVITIES:

Fill in the following table. The primary movement is supplied and is marked by an asterisk. The accommodating movements for the other two bones must be provided. For example, when the humerus is abducted, the scapula must rotate upwardly, and the clavicle must elevate.

Humerus	Scapula	Clavicle
Adduction*		
	Upward rotation*	
	Posterior tilt*	
Extension*		
	Abduction*	

	Humerus	Scapula	Clavicle
Horizontal extension*			
Medial rotation*			
Lateral rotation*			

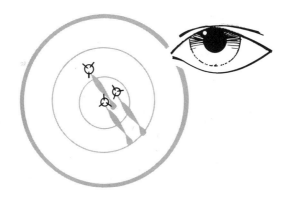

KINESTHESIS

CONCEPT 25: Reflexes for skeletal muscles are classified into two main categories—exteroceptive and proprioceptive.

CONCEPT 26: Resetting the length of the muscle spindle is accomplished via the stretch reflex.

CONCEPT 27: The stretch (postural) reflex is a fundamental reflex.

CONCEPT 28: Kinesthesis is reinforced by visual information.

CONCEPT 25: KINESTHESIS

REFLEXES FOR SKELETAL MUSCLES ARE CLASSIFIED INTO TWO MAIN CATEGORIES — EXTEROCEPTIVE AND PROPRIOCEPTIVE

INFORMATION:

1. *Exteroceptive reflexes* are those initiated by stimuli from our external environment. Some examples are the extensor-thrust reflex, flexor reflex, and crossed-extensor reflex.
2. *Proprioceptive reflexes* are those initiated by stimuli from the internal environment of our skeletal muscles and joints. The modalities of stretch, tension change, and pressure put these reflexes into action. Examples include the stretch or myotatic reflex.

RATIONALE:

The extensor-thrust reflex is initiated by pressure received in our *cutaneous receptors,* causing a reflex contraction of our powerful extensor muscles in the legs. The mere standing or walking in daily activities will elicit the performance of this reflex.

Flexor reflexes are most important because these are initiated by pain and protect the body from harm. The hot stove burn which causes sudden withdrawal of the upper limb is a classic example. This reflex is often referred to as the withdrawal reflex.

A cross-extensor reflex is somewhat more complicated than the above two. However, it plays a significant role in many activities. Protection from pain in one limb withdrawn from the source causes, by way of this reflex, the extensor muscles in the other limb to contract for support. Alternating muscle contractions in the lower limbs during walking, running, and the like employ this reflex.

Proprioceptive reflexes are discussed in subsequent concepts.

ACTIVITIES:

Give the specific exteroceptive reflex type (extensor-thrust, flexor, cross-extensor) illustrated by each of the following activities.

57

Action	Type of Reflex
Blinking when a foreign substance touches the eyeball	Flexor
Jumping as a result of hearing a loud noise	_____
Retracting a foot from the hot pavement	_____
Standing in a line at the bank	_____
Walking into an icy-cold shower (response of the skin)	_____

CONCEPT 26: KINESTHESIS

RESETTING THE LENGTH OF THE MUSCLE SPINDLE IS ACCOMPLISHED VIA THE STRETCH REFLEX

INFORMATION:

1. Kinesthesis is defined as the perception of muscular movement and the relative position of the performer's body parts in space.
2. The muscle spindles, which respond when skeletal muscles are stretched, constitute a major group of proprioceptors which receive information concerning muscular movement.
3. The muscle spindles are located throughout muscle mass and are activated when the muscle they occupy is stretched.
4. Some mechanism must exist whereby the stretched muscle spindle can return to its resting length or to some new length.

RATIONALE:

One purpose of the muscle spindles is to inform the central nervous system that a skeletal muscle has become elongated (stretched). By reflex action, the elongated muscle contracts. However, if the muscle spindle remains elongated, it continues to send out stimuli and, by reflex, will cause the muscle to continue to contract. The elongated spindle must return to its resting length as the elongated muscle contracts.

When a muscle spindle is elongated, it generates action potential which travels, via an afferent neuron, to the spinal cord. A component of this impulse is carried along an alpha efferent neuron and causes the elongated muscle to contract. Another component travels along a gamma efferent neuron to the muscle spindle where contractile elements (intrafusal fibers) within the muscle spindle are caused to contract. The muscle spindle returns to its resting length or to a new length, thus resetting the sensory complex.

59

ACTIVITIES:

1. Label the following diagram. The parts to be labelled are listed at the right.

Muscle   Spindle

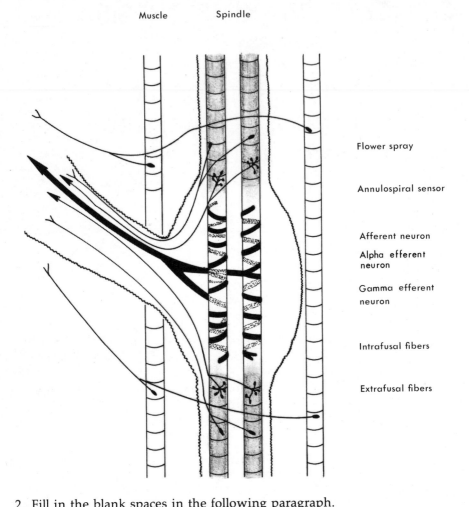

Flower spray

Annulospiral sensor

Afferent neuron

Alpha efferent neuron

Gamma efferent neuron

Intrafusal fibers

Extrafusal fibers

2. Fill in the blank spaces in the following paragraph.

When a muscle becomes elongated, its muscle spindles also become _____. This physical change causes the _____ and _____ to become stimulated. Action potential is created and travels to the CNS via an _____. Some of the action potential returns to the muscle spindle via a _____. Contractile elements known as _____ _____ within the muscle spindle are stimulated and the muscle spindle returns to its _____ _____. Simultaneously, the elongated skeletal muscle _____ _____.

CONCEPT 27: KINESTHESIS

THE STRETCH (POSTURAL) REFLEX IS A FUNDAMENTAL REFLEX

INFORMATION:

1. The stretch reflex is generally triggered by the muscle spindles. (See Concept 26.)
2. The stretch reflex is important in the maintenance of upright posture in humans.

RATIONALE:

Basically, the maintenance of upright posture in humans is a function of reflex action. As the center of gravity of the body drifts toward any margin of the base of support, the muscles in the body segment closest to the center of the base of support become stretched. The muscle spindles in those muscles are also stretched, triggering the stretch reflex.

Action potentials are created in the stretched muscle spindles and travel to the CNS via an afferent neuron. A component of that action potential returns along an alpha efferent neuron to the stretched muscles. The stretched muscles contract and pull the body mass back into the center of the base of support. Stability is regained and the body is prevented from falling off balance.

ACTIVITIES:

A performer is walking on a balance beam. Her center of gravity shifts to the right. She is in danger of falling off the beam. Fill in the blank spaces in the following paragraph.

As her body shifts to the right, the muscles on the _____ side of her body become _____. The involved muscle spindles also become _____, creating _____ _____, which travels to the CNS via an _____ neuron. A component of this action potential returns to the stretched muscles via an _____ _____ _____. Contractile elements in the stretch muscles contract, pulling the _____ back into the _____ of the base of support. _____ is re-established.

61

CONCEPT 28: KINESTHESIS

KINESTHESIS IS REINFORCED BY VISUAL INFORMATION

INFORMATION:

1. As stated previously, man possesses two general types of receptors specific to skeletal movement; however, one of the most important receptors affecting human movement is the eye. (See Concept 25.)
2. Of all the many receptors possessed by man, the eye is the most significant. In fact, 80 to 90 per cent of our environment is thought to be perceived through visual stimuli.

RATIONALE:

Man seldom relies upon kinesthetic perception alone. The five major senses all aid in reinforcing man's perception. The diver reinforces his kinesthetic information through *visual cues* by looking for the surface of the water as he aligns his body for entry, or he pinpoints a visual cue on the ceiling before performing acrobatic skills.

When visual information is reduced or absent, man as a compensatory organism relies upon his other senses — especially kinesthesis and hearing — in order to maintain his balance and posture.

ACITIVITIES:

1. Why are golfers instructed to keep their eyes on the ball during the golf swing?

2. What type of information informs the golfer, prior to contact, that his swing was imperfect?

3. Why do competitive divers request that the surface of the water be ruffled immediately prior to their dives?

4. Why do people recently blinded get instructions in travel-training (mobility of the blind)?

5. Standing with eyes open, lift one foot to the front and swing the free leg about. Repeat the performance with the eyes closed. Which was easier? Why?

SECTION TWO

THE PRODUCTION OF MOTION

FORCE

CONCEPT 29: FORCE

MUSCLES CAUSE MOVEMENT AT THE JOINTS BY PULLING ON BONES

INFORMATION:

1. A *force* is defined as a push or pull.
2. During *concentric contraction* muscles produce force. (See Concept 6.)
3. Muscles pull on bones to cause motion at the joint they span.
4. The *line of pull* of a muscle is along its long dimension or along a straight line between its attachments.

RATIONALE:

Because muscles are members of a lever system, they produce movement at the joints they span by exerting a pull on the bone which moves. The movement of the bone is toward or away from the line of pull of the muscle.

ACTIVITIES:

Indicate the following information by use of arrows in the labelled diagrams.

a. Line of pull of muscle.

b. Direction of movement at the bone.

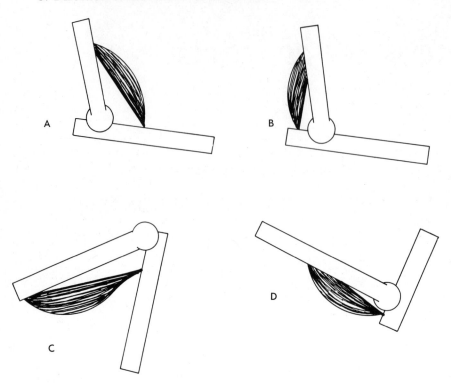

CONCEPT 30: FORCE

TO BEGIN A MOTOR ACTIVITY, A FORCE MUST BE PRODUCED WITHIN THE BODY IN ORDER TO OVERCOME INERTIA

INFORMATION:

1. The *inertia* of a body is directly proportional to its *mass*.
2. In order to overcome inertia, a force must be exerted on a mass.
3. Motor activity involves the movement of the total body or its component parts.
4. The force which commonly overcomes inertia in motor activities is provided by muscular contraction.
5. *Work* = force × distance ($W = Fd$).

RATIONALE:

When a body or a segment of a body is set in motion, the tendency of the body to remain at rest (inertia) must be overcome. To accomplish this end result, a force must be provided. Such force commonly is provided by concentric, and at times eccentric, muscle contraction, acting upon bones with sufficient force to set them in motion.

Even in events such as diving, in which gravity pulls the body downward, inertia must first be overcome by muscular contraction.

A muscle creates pull by contracting along its long dimension. Typically, muscles contract up to one-half their resting length. As a muscle exerts a pull (force) while contracting up to one-half its resting length (distance), the muscle accomplishes work and can pull a bone around an axis of motion. The amount of pull produced by a muscle is proportional to its cross-sectional area. A muscle at optimal length can exert a pull of approximately 42 pounds per square inch, or 3 kilograms per cm² of muscle.

ACTIVITIES:

A muscle has a resting length of six inches. The muscle has a cross-sectional area of 1¼ square inches. The muscle can exert a pull of 42 lbs. per square inch of cross section.

69

How many pounds of pull are exerted by this contracting muscle?

How much work does the muscle perform while contracting?

$$\left(\frac{\text{inch-pounds}}{12} = \text{foot-pounds}\right)$$

What is accomplished by this work?

CONCEPT 31: FORCE

DESIRED MOVEMENT IS OFTEN THE RESULT OF THE SUMMATION OF FORCES

INFORMATION:

1. The principle of summation of forces says that "whenever a sequence of movements is employed to impart momentum to an object, each lever must make its contribution at the instant of impact or the instant of release."
2. Levers with the greatest mass possess the greatest inertia and must move first in the sequence.
3. Smaller levers possess less inertia and move last in the sequence.

RATIONALE:

When an angler casts a plug onto the surface of a pond, three levers produce the forces which impart momentum to the plug. These are the shoulder, the elbow, and the wrist. All three levers must make their contribution at the instant the plug starts forward.

Since the shoulder has the greatest mass, it has the greatest inertia to be overcome and must be the first lever to begin to move. The elbow has greater inertia than the wrist and must be the next lever to begin to move. Because the wrist has the least mass, it has the least inertia and is the fastest moving lever. It is the last lever in the sequence to begin to move. In this manner, all three levers can make their contribution at the moment the plug starts forward.

ACTIVITIES:

1. Five levers which contribute to the momentum of the left fist upon impact with a punching bag are the elbow, shoulder, vertebral column, hip, and the right knee. Arrange these five levers in the order in which they must begin to move.

2. The levers which contribute to the velocity of a golf ball are the elbow, wrist, shoulder, vertebral column, and the hip. Arrange these five levers in the order in which they must begin to move.

CONCEPT 32: FORCE

CENTRIFUGAL FORCE INVOLVES A SPECIAL APPLICATION OF THE LAW OF INERTIA

INFORMATION:

1. *Centrifugal force* attempts to pull an object out of its orbit.
2. Newton's first law indicates that an object set in motion travels in a straight line.

RATIONALE:

The hammer thrower swings the hammer for several revolutions. He feels a definite pull on his arms and shoulders as the hammer attempts to escape from its orbit about his shoulders. This pull is centrifugal force.

The physicist argues that centrifugal force is a "false force" and does not exist. His reasoning is that once the hammer, or any other orbiting object, is released from bondage, it leaves the orbit and travels in a straight line. Such a released object is subject to Newton's law of inertia. Therefore, centrifugal force is merely a special application of the law of inertia. Moreover, centrifugal force is provided by the mass of the orbiting object, and inertia and mass are directly proportional factors.

ACTIVITIES:

1. A softball pitcher employs a windmill wind-up so that the arm travels in one revolution about the glenohumeral joint before the ball is released.
    a. What force causes an outward pull on the arm during the wind up?

    b. Upon its release from the hand, does the ball continue to orbit? If not, describe the path of the ball.

2. A waterskier is pulled behind a boat which makes a wide turn.
   a. He feels an increased pull on his arms as the boat begins to turn. What force causes this pull?

   b. If the skier releases the rope in order to make a landing near shore, will he circle around out into the lake or travel in a straight line into the shore?

CONCEPT 33: FORCE

THERE ARE THREE METHODS OF INDUCING ROTATION IN AN OBJECT

INFORMATION:

1. *Rotation* is angular movement on the part of an object and occurs around an axis of *motion.* The movement is often less than a complete revolution of 360 degrees.
2. Rotation may be induced in an object, including the total human body.
3. An object in motion, including the human body, possesses linear velocity. One method of inducing rotation is to check linear velocity at an extremity.
4. A second method of inducing rotation is to employ the principle of transfer of momentum. Momentum may be transferred from a part of the body to the total body.
5. A third method of inducing rotation is to employ eccentric thrust. *Eccentric thrust* involves a force striking an object at some point other than its center of gravity.

RATIONALE:

During running, the human body possesses linear velocity. When the toe is stubbed on a rock, linear velocity is checked at an extremity. Rotation is induced, the foot acts as an axis of motion for the total body, and the torso rotates forward and downward toward the ground.

During certain diving and tumbling events, the performer wishes to induce rotation in the total body in order to execute somersaults or twisting maneuvers. To accomplish these, parts of the body are moved in the direction of the intended rotation. In performing a somersault, the trunk is flexed at the instant of take-off. The body, not yet departed from the supporting surface, cannot move in the opposite direction, since the mass of the body is still connected to the mass of the earth. Immediately after takeoff, the momentum of the flexed trunk is transferred to the total body, which follows in the direction of the flexed trunk. The result is forward rotation, a somersault.

Eccentric thrust involves a force transmitted to an object at some point other than its center of gravity. Batted baseballs rotate because the bat strikes the ball at a point removed from the center of gravity. A thrown ball rotates because the force of the body is transmitted via the hand to a point on the ball other than its center of gravity.

ACTIVITIES:

Complete the following table. An event is listed. Place a check mark in the correct box for the cause of rotation in the listed event.

Event	Checked Linear Velocity	Transfer of Momentum	Eccentric Thrust
Diver arches back at takeoff		√	
Batted ball exhibits topspin			
Runner trips on hurdle			
"Hooked" golf ball			
High jumper leans back at takeoff			
Hopping fastball pitch in baseball			
Turntable on trampoline			
Double forward somersault dive			
Boy stubs toe—lands on face			
Backspin on golf shot			

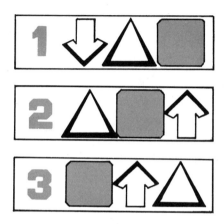

LEVERS

CONCEPT 34: LEVERS

THREE CLASSES OF LEVERS ARE INVOLVED IN HUMAN MOVEMENT

INFORMATION:

1. The three parts of a lever are the *force point* (the exact point where the effort is applied), the *resistance point* (the exact point on which the resistance acts), and the *fulcrum* (the axis of motion).
2. The *resistance point* in a human body lever frequently is the center of gravity of the moving body segment plus any external weights.
3. The *force arm* of a lever is the distance from the force point to the *axis of motion* (fulcrum).
4. The *resistance arm* of a lever is the distance from the resistance point to the *axis of motion*.
5. The relative arrangement of the force point, resistance point, and fulcrum distinguishes the three classes of levers.

RATIONALE:

A lever is a machine capable of performing work. Effort (force) is applied at one point, and a resistance at some other point is moved. The lever pivots about an axis of motion called the fulcrum.

A *first-class lever* has its fulcrum at some location between the resistance point and the force point. Example: see-saw. A *second-class lever* has its resistance point at some location between the force point and the fulcrum. Example: wheelbarrow. A *third-class lever* has its force point at some location between the resistance point and the fulcrum. Example: shovel.

A body part which moves, acts as a lever. The joint (fulcrum) is the fixed axis of motion about which *angular motion* occurs. The force is provided by a contracting muscle, and the insertion of that muscle into the moving bone is the force point. The resistance in the system is commonly the pull of gravity. The resistance point is the center of gravity of the moving body segment plus any external objects attached to that segment.

ACTIVITIES:

1. Draw and label the three classes of levers.

   (1)   (2)   (3)

CONCEPT 35: LEVERS

CERTAIN MECHANICAL FACTORS UNDERGO REDUCTIONS OR GAINS IN LEVER SYSTEMS

INFORMATION:

1. Different lever classes provide increases or decreases in three mechanical factors. These are force, speed of movement, and range of motion.
2. A reduction in one of these factors is accompanied by a gain in one or both of the remaining factors.
3. The relative lengths of the force arm and the resistance arm aid in understanding which factors are improved or reduced. (See Concept 34.)
4. All of the above statements are in accord with one of the most fundamental physical laws, the conservation of energy, which states that energy can be neither created nor destroyed but may change its form; that is, energy is conserved.

RATIONALE:

When a simple machine such as a lever is employed, certain factors are either gained or reduced. If a first-class lever has a longer force arm than its resistance arm, a gain in force will result. However, there will be an accompanying reduction in range and speed of motion. The resistance arm moves a shorter distance than the force arm and moves slower.

A second-class lever always has a longer force arm than its resistance arm. This class of lever produces a gain in force. More resistance can be overcome than force applied, but the resistance arm moves slower through a shorter range of motion. Because a greater force arm exists, less force is needed to overcome a greater resistance.

The third-class lever always has a resistance arm longer than its force arm. Such levers suffer a reduction in force. A relatively light resistance is moved rapidly through a longer range of motion because the amount of force applied exceeds the amount of resistance moved.

When a first-class lever has a longer resistance arm than its force arm, there will be a reduction in force. However, a gain in range and speed of motion will be realized. Should a force greater than the resistance be applied to such a lever, the resistance arm will move rapidly through a range of motion greater than that of the force arm.

ACTIVITIES:

Study each diagram and identify the class of lever. Write in the factor(s) gained or reduced in each diagram.

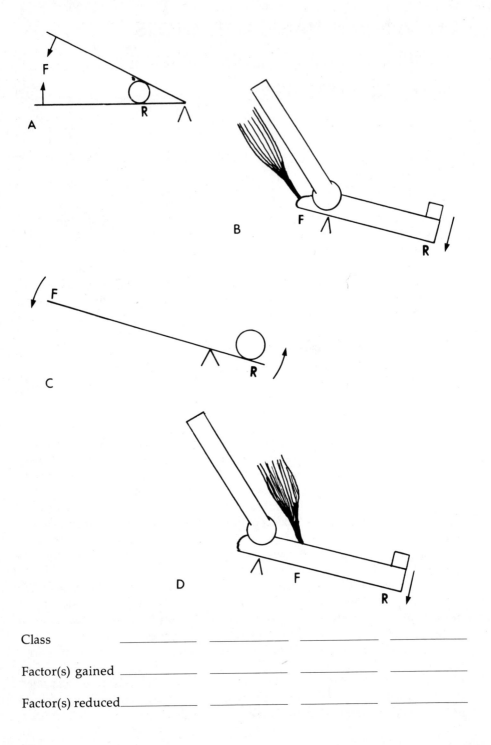

Class _____ _____ _____ _____

Factor(s) gained _____ _____ _____ _____

Factor(s) reduced _____ _____ _____ _____

CONCEPT 36: LEVERS

THE ELBOW JOINT IS AN EXAMPLE WHERE ALL THREE CLASSES OF LEVERS ARE FOUND

INFORMATION:

1. A human body lever may consist of one or more moving bones (resistance), a joint (axis of motion), and one or more contracting muscles (force).
2. The *resistance point* of a body segment is normally $3/7$ of the distance from the proximal end, if no external weights are attached.

RATIONALE:

There are three primary flexor muscles and one primary extensor muscle which move the forearm at the elbow. The elbow is the axis, and the forearm is the resistance.

Elbow extension involves a first-class lever. The triceps inserts (force point) onto the olecranon process of the ulna which protrudes above the joint. The center of gravity (resistance point) of the forearm is $3/7$ of the distance from the joint to the finger tips. Thus, a force, fulcrum, and resistance relationship exists.

The action of the brachioradialis muscle at the elbow joint serves as a second-class lever. The muscle inserts (force point) into the radius at a point beyond the resistance point (center of gravity). Thus, a fulcrum, resistance, and force relationship exists.

Both the biceps and the brachialis muscles act to construct a third-class lever. They insert into the forearm at points which are between the joint (axis) and the center of gravity (resistance point). Thus, a fulcrum, force, and resistance relationship exists.

ACTIVITIES:

Label the following diagram. Draw in the approximate muscle attachments and indicate the location of the force point, resistance point, and fulcrum. Classify the type of lever involved and indicate the factors gained or reduced. (See Concept 35.)

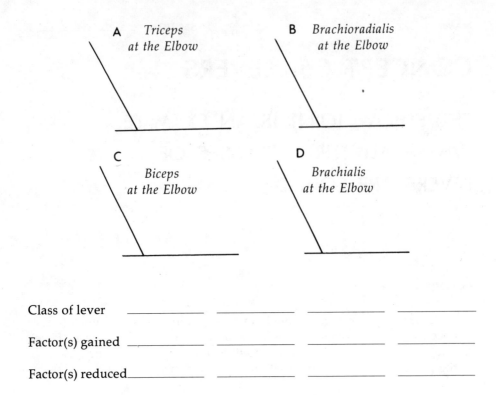

A   *Triceps*
at the Elbow

B   *Brachioradialis*
at the Elbow

C

Biceps
at the Elbow

D

Brachialis
at the Elbow

Class of lever   _____   _____   _____   _____

Factor(s) gained   _____   _____   _____   _____

Factor(s) reduced _____   _____   _____   _____

CONCEPT 37: LEVERS

ADDING EXTERNAL WEIGHT CAN CHANGE THE CLASS OF A LEVER

INFORMATION:

1. Levers are classified according to the relative location of the force point, resistance point, and fulcrum.
2. Adding external weights to a body segment can cause a shift in the location of its center of gravity (resistance point), which could result in a change in the class of lever.

RATIONALE:

The brachioradialis muscle inserts into (force point) the styloid process, located near the distal end of the radius. The center of gravity of the forearm (resistance point) is between the force point and the joint when the hands are empty. The brachioradialis serves as a second-class lever.

When external weight is held in the hands, the center of gravity of the forearm shifts toward the hands. If the weight is sufficent, the center of gravity shifts to a point beyond the insertion of the brachioradialis. The class of lever for the brachioradialis muscle now shifts from second- to third-class. It is the change in the position of the resistance point that is responsible for this shift.

ACTIVITIES:

Consider the following drawings. Locate the position of the fulcrum, the force point, and the resistance point in each drawing. Classify the type of lever involved and indicate the factors gained or reduced.

85

A

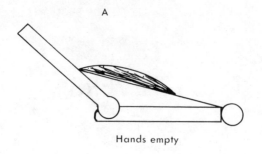

Hands empty

B

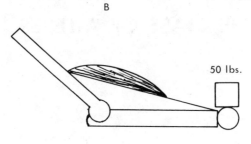

50 lbs.

External weight in hands

Class of lever

Factor(s) gained

Factor(s) reduced

CONCEPT 38: LEVERS

MOVEMENT OCCURS WHEN LEVERS ARE UNBALANCED

INFORMATION:

1. The law of levers states that a lever will balance when the product of force multiplied by the length of the *force arm* equals the product of the resistance multiplied by the length of the *resistance arm* ($F \times FA = R \times RA$), when these variables are perpendicular to one another.
2. When a lever is balanced, no movement occurs. In order for movement to occur, the lever must be unbalanced in favor of the force or resistance.
3. Either the force (muscular contraction) or the resistance (the weight of the object) can cause movement on the part of human body levers. The movement will occur at the involved joints, which serve as axes of motion.

RATIONALE:

During motor activities body levers are seldom balanced. Levers must be unbalanced in order for movements to occur at joints. The levers may be unbalanced in favor of force or resistance.

The chin-up serves as a good example of this concept. In order to pull the body weight up to the bar, the product of ($F \times FA$) must be greater than ($R \times RA$). In order to lower the body to the starting position, force must be reduced so that ($F \times FA$) becomes less than ($R \times RA$).

There are activities in which force and resistance work together in order to produce motion. During the downswing in the golf drive, both muscular effort and gravity cause the resistance (golf club) to move.

ACTIVITIES:

1. Two children simultaneously climb onto the plank of a seesaw which is parallel to the ground. James weighs 60 pounds and sits at a point 5 feet from the fulcrum. John, who weighs 70 pounds, takes a seat 4 feet from the fulcrum. Will the lever move? If so, which child will move upward, and why?
   a.
   b.
2. During running, the femur is flexed at 90° and parallel to the ground.

Considering only the illiopsoas as the sole flexor of the femur, answer the following questions. Given: The insertion of the illiopsoas is 2 inches from the joint; the weight of the leg is 25 pounds; and the center of gravity of the leg is 14 inches from the joint.

a. What formula is appropriate in solving this type of problem?

b. What is the length of the force arm in feet?

c. What is the length of the resistance arm in feet?

d. What is the amount of resistance?

e. How many pounds of pull must the illiopsoas generate in order to flex the femur?

f. What class of lever is involved?

g. What factor is reduced in this class of lever? (See Concept 35.)

CONCEPT 39: LEVERS

IDENTIFICATION OF THE TRUE FORCE ARM AND THE TRUE RESISTANCE ARM CLEARLY INTERPRETS THE LAW OF LEVERS

INFORMATION:

1. *Torque* is a lever action using the joint as an axis, with muscles providing the force and with body segments or external weights providing the resistance.
2. The *true force arm* is defined as the *perpendicular* distance from the *line of pull of the muscle* to the axis of motion (the joint). The line of pull of a muscle lies in a straight line between its two attachments.
3. The *true resistance arm* is defined as the *perpendicular* distance from the *line of pull of the resistance* to the axis of motion (the joint). The line of pull of resistance ordinarily is a vertical line.
4. The amount of torque occurring at a joint can be measured if the following factors are known:
    a. the amount of force applied to the bone
    b. the length of the true force arm
    c. the amount of resistance to be overcome
    d. the length of the true resistance arm
5. The law of levers should be amended to read that a lever is balanced if force times true force arm equals resistance times true resistance arm. (F × TFA = R × TRA.) (See Concept 38.)

RATIONALE:

The law of levers previously stated in Concept 38 is oversimplified. Consider two children operating a seesaw with the plank upon which Child A sits too short to rest on the ground.

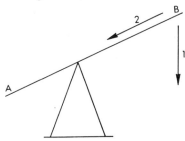

In this case, all of the force produced by the weight of Child B does not move him downward. Only a portion of the force moves Child B downward (1), while another force is directed along the plank (2) and would, if great enough, shear the bolt holding the plank to the fulcrum. Consequently, this demonstrates that only a portion of the force in a lever system produces the desired motion (Child B moving downward).

In Concept 38, the force arm and the resistance arm were measured along the lever (see below).

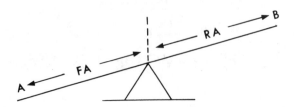

All of the force produced by gravity acting on Child B is not used to produce the desired motion. Some was lost because it was directed along the plank toward the fulcrum.

The amended law of levers includes the true force arm and the true resistance arm necessary for producing torque. The diagram below represents an interpretation of the *true force arm* (CD).

B represents the force point, C the axis of rotation, and the dotted line (CD) represents the true force arm. It is apparent, if measured, that line CD is shorter than BC, or that the true force arm is shorter than the force arm. The true force arm thus represents the component of force that provides motion at the fulcrum (joint). Child A represents the resistance, line AC the resistance arm, and line CE the *true resistance arm*. As in the force arms, the true resistance arm is shorter than the resistance arm. Thus, not all the force (weight of Child A) is directed to the desired outcome, causing his end of the plank to descend further.

ACTIVITIES:

1. Draw the true force arm and the true resistance arm in the following muscle diagram.

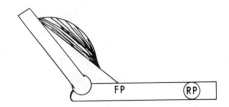

2. Torque provided by a contracting muscle is determined by multiplying F × TFA, resulting in units of foot-pounds. In the drawing above for activity 1, the force = 200 pounds and the TFA = ½ inch. What amount of torque is produced in the system to flex the forearm at the elbow (in foot-pound units)?

   Answer:

3. A heavy resistance can also cause a lever to move downward. Example: a heavy weight can cause a flexed elbow to extend. Torque provided by a resistance is determined by multiplying R × TRA. In activity 2, if R = 50 pounds and TRA = 15 inches, what is the amount of torque producing extension at the elbow?

   Answer:

CONCEPT 40: LEVERS

THE WHEEL AND AXLE AND FIXED PULLEY MACHINES OF THE MUSCULO-SKELETAL SYSTEM ARE SIMPLY SPECIAL CASES OF THE LEVER SYSTEM

INFORMATION:

1. When the force point is applied to the axle, the force arm is shortened, and force is sacrificed for speed; however, if the force point is applied to the wheel, the force arm is lengthened and speed is sacrificed for force.
2. The sliding of a tendon around a prominent marking establishes a first-class lever system. This machine acts to change the direction of the line of pull of a muscle in addition to increasing its angle of pull.

RATIONALE:

Like most other levers in the body, the wheel and axle serve for gaining speed and range of motion at the expense of force. The twisting or rotatory movements about the longitudinal axis of a bony part are examples of this simple machine action. Investigation demonstrates that we possess both types where force is applied to the rim and where force is applied to the axle.

The fixed pulley is often found in the musculoskeletal system. Two important events occur in the fixed pulley. As the line of pull of a muscle is changed, the true force arm increases, and the angle of pull increases. Diagram A illustrates an increased true force arm, while Diagram B illustrates an increased angle of pull.

Diagram A   Diagram B

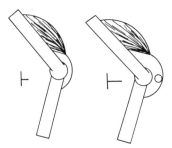
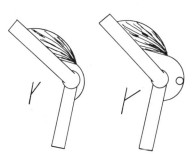

ACTIVITIES:

1. Describe two wheel and axle machines within the human body, one with the force applied to the wheel and the other with the force applied to the axle.
   a.
   b.
2. Cite five muscles whose tendons turn about a prominent bony marking and develop into a fixed pulley system.
   a.
   b.
   c.
   d.
   e.

TORQUE

CONCEPT 41: Motion can occur at joints only when levers are unbalanced.

CONCEPT 42: Torque is the magnitude of twist around an axis of rotation.

CONCEPT 43: Muscular contraction (force) results in torque at human joints.

CONCEPT 44: A resistance (force of gravity) can cause torque at human joints.

CONCEPT 45: Additional muscle force is needed to move a joint when the length of the true resistance arm or the amount of resistance is increased.

CONCEPT 46: Forces acting on joints can be divided into two components—rotatory and nonrotatory.

CONCEPT 47: Nonrotatory components of muscle force (pull) and resistance yield "undesired" actions.

CONCEPT 48: The angle of muscle pull changes as joint movement occurs.

CONCEPT 49: The human body is mechanically inefficient.

CONCEPT 50: The behavior of levers can be explained in terms of moment of force and moment of inertia.

CONCEPT 41: TORQUE

MOTION CAN OCCUR AT JOINTS ONLY WHEN LEVERS ARE UNBALANCED

INFORMATION:

1. *Torque* is the product of a force transmitted across perpendicular distance.
2. Either the pull of a contracting muscle or the pull of some resistance can result in torque.

RATIONALE:

Motion can occur at a joint only when the involved lever is unbalanced. If the lever is balanced, no motion results at the joint.

Using the elbow joint as an example, let us consider the arm in the anatomical position. The elbow can be flexed only when the torque produced by the contracting elbow flexors (F × TFA) is greater than the torque produced by the weight of the forearm (R × TRA).

In the same manner, the pull of gravity can move the flexed elbow into extension only when the torque produced by R × TRA exceeds the torque produced by the elbow flexors; that is, if we can "partial out" the phenomenon of eccentric contraction of the elbow flexors. (See Concept 6.)

ACTIVITIES:

1. Diagnose the following torque situation. A subject in the *supine* position is attempting to hold a bilateral leg lift position.

$$
\begin{aligned}
\text{Given:} \quad & F = 500 \text{ pounds} \\
& TFA = 2 \text{ inches} \\
& R = 50 \text{ pounds} \\
& TRA = 15 \text{ inches}
\end{aligned}
$$

Will the legs continue to rise through flexion, or will they drop to the floor?

2. Complete the following table. Columns I and II list the possible movements. Columns III, IV, V, and VI provide necessary data. In Column VII, list the movement from Column I or II, which, in fact, does occur.

I	II	III	IV	V	VI	VII
Motion Caused by Force	*Motion Caused by Resistance*	*F*	*TFA*	*R*	*TRA*	*Resulting Motion*
Elbow flexion	Elbow extension	50	1"	15	9"	Extension
Wrist flexion	Wrist extension	25	1½"	3	3"	_____
Arm abduction	Arm adduction	100	2"	15	15"	_____
Dorsiflexion	Plantar flexion	200	3"	5	6"	_____

CONCEPT 42: TORQUE

TORQUE IS THE MAGNITUDE OF TWIST AROUND AN AXIS OF ROTATION

INFORMATION:

1. *Torque* or twist can be rotatory (angular) movement in any plane about an axis of motion.
2. To more clearly understand torque, *force* will be continuously used interchangeably with muscular contraction, while *resistance* will be the pull of gravity, the opposing force.
3. Torque occurs when bones move around each other at joints which serve as axes of movement.

RATIONALE:

Torque occurs when bones move at joints. For example, when flexing the elbow, the proximal end of the ulna rotates around the spool-shaped distal end of the humerus. When abducting the arm at the shoulder, the humerus follows a rotatory (angular) path within the glenoid fossa of the scapula. Thus, the angular motion of a bone moving around a joint falls within the definition and understanding of torque.

ACTIVITIES:

Column I has a list of activities occurring in daily life. Place a "Yes" in column II if the activity is an example of torque. If the answer for column II is "Yes," enter the axis of motion in column III.

I	II	III
	Torque,	
Activity	*Yes, or No*	*Axis of Motion*
Working a woodscrew into a plank	Yes	Long axis of woodscrew
Pulling a nail from a plank	_____	_____
Wringing out a wet towel	_____	_____
Extending the elbow	_____	_____

I	II	III
	Torque,	
Activity	*Yes, or No*	*Axis of Motion*
Stepping on an auto gas pedal	————	————————
Riding down a rollercoaster	————	————————
Turning on the TV	————	————————
Standing at attention	————	————————
Shoulder action in forehand tennis stroke	————	————————
Chewing gum	————	————————
Drinking through a straw	————	————————

CONCEPT 43: TORQUE

MUSCULAR CONTRACTION (FORCE) RESULTS IN TORQUE AT HUMAN JOINTS

INFORMATION:

1. The amount of torque produced by a contracting muscle is determined by multiplying the amount of force (pounds) developed by the contracting muscle(s) by the length of the *true force arm*. The answer is expressed in units of foot-pounds. (See Concept 39.)
2. When a muscle contracts to cause motion at a joint, the pull produced by the muscle is transmitted across perpendicular distance to the involved joint, and the resulting torque produces angular motion.

RATIONALE:

Movements occurring at joints are the result of torque. The force causing movements at joints is commonly the result of *concentric contraction.* (See Concept 6.)

The longer the true force arm, the greater the amount of torque available to produce motion. (See Concept 42.) This becomes obvious when a mechanic selects a longer handled wrench to remove a rusty bolt. Unfortunately, muscles in the human body attach themselves to bones in close proximity to the joints, resulting in short true force arms. As a consequence, a lesser amount of torque is produced for the desired angular motion. Therefore, much of the pull of the muscle may be expended in serving some other purpose.

ACTIVITIES:

1. Complete the following table: Column I lists a constant force of 300 lbs. of pull produced by a contracting muscle. Column II lists varying true force arms. (Note: Convert inches to decimal portions of one foot.) In column III, list the amount of torque in foot-pounds which is produced to move the joint.

101

I	II	III
Force	*TFA*	*Torque Produced*
300 lbs.	⅛" (.01 feet)	3 ft.-lbs.
300 lbs.	¼"	
300 lbs.	½"	
300 lbs.	¾"	
300 lbs.	1"	
300 lbs.	1½"	

2. For activity 1, answer the following.
   a. Which TFA produced the least torque?
   b. Which TFA produced the most torque?
   c. Explain the relationship which exists between the length of the TFA and the amount of torque produced.

CONCEPT 44: TORQUE

A RESISTANCE (FORCE OF GRAVITY) CAN CAUSE TORQUE AT HUMAN JOINTS

INFORMATION:

1. A heavy resistance can produce enough torque to cause the joints to move. If the abducted arm is subjected to the pull of gravity, that extremity will become adducted.
2. When gravity or some other resistance pulls on a body segment, that resistive force is transmitted across a perpendicular distance (*true resistance arm*) to the involved joint, and the resulting torque produces motion.

RATIONALE:

Many human movements occur, in part or in whole, when some resistance causes a body segment to move at a joint. A commonly employed resistive force is gravity. Gravity exerts all of its force on the center of gravity (resistance point) of the body segment. If no external weights are added to a body segment, its resistance point is located $3/7$ of the distance from the proximal end.

The resistive force is transmitted across a perpendicular distance (true resistance arm) to the involved joint. Torque is produced, and motion occurs. The longer the true resistance arm, the greater the quantity of torque produced. A weight at the end of a longer lever will swing down faster than the same weight at the end of a shorter lever.

Unfortunately, in the human body the true resistance arms typically are longer than the true force arms. The torque produced by the resistance is considerable. Therefore, the muscles must produce great amounts of pull in order to lift relatively light resistances.

ACTIVITIES:

1. Complete the following table. Column I lists a constant resistance of 100 lbs. Column II lists varying true resistance arms. In column III, list the amount of torque which is produced at the joint in foot-pounds.

103

I	II	III
Resistance	*TRA*	*Torque Produced*
100 lbs.	7"(.58 feet)	58 ft.-lbs.
100 lbs.	8"	
100 lbs.	9"	
100 lbs.	10"	
100 lbs.	11"	
100 lbs.	12"	

2. Questions regarding activity I.
    a. Which TRA produced the least torque?

    b. Which TRA produced the most torque?

    c. What type of relationship exists between the length of the TRA and the amount of torque produced?

CONCEPT 45: TORQUE

ADDITIONAL MUSCLE FORCE IS NEEDED TO MOVE A JOINT WHEN THE LENGTH OF THE TRUE RESISTANCE ARM OR THE AMOUNT OF RESISTANCE IS INCREASED

INFORMATION:

1. The *torque* produced by a resistance is the product of the amount of resistance multiplied by the length of the *true resistance arm*.
2. If an external weight is added to a body segment, the center of gravity (*resistance point*) shifts toward the location of that external weight. (See Concept 37.)
3. A weight added to the hand, therefore, increases the resistance (weight) of the arm and lengthens the true resistance arm.

RATIONALE:

It is easier to raise a balky window by standing close, rather than at arm's length, because the length of the resistance arm is short when standing near the window.

Anytime a heavy weight needs to be lifted, the center of gravity of the person doing the lifting is moved as close as possible to the weight. As a consequence, the true resistance arm is made shorter so that the muscle effort (force) is directed primarily to the desired goal, lifting the weight as efficiently as possible.

ACTIVITIES:

1. Situation A.   The deltoid is flexing the humerus and the hands are empty. The glenohumeral joint is the axis of motion. Using the formula F×TFA =

105

R×TRA, how many pounds of pull must the deltoid exert in order to flex the humerus?

TFA = 2"
R = 20 lbs.   Answer:
TRA = 15"

2. **Situation B.**   The deltoid again is flexing the humerus, but the hands contain a 50 lb. dumbbell. The resistance has increased, and the length of the true resistance arm also has increased. How many pounds of pull must the deltoid now exert in order to flex the humerus?

TFA = 2"
R = 70 lbs.   Answer:
TRA = 36"

3. Questions.
   a. What two factors cause the increase in force required in Situation B?

   b. Is the amount of force calculated in activities 1 and 2 sufficient to move the joint? (See Concept 41.)

CONCEPT 46: TORQUE

FORCES ACTING ON JOINTS CAN BE DIVIDED INTO TWO COMPONENTS—ROTATORY AND NONROTATORY

INFORMATION:

1. The force provided by a contracting muscle or by gravity (resistance) is subdivided into two components—rotatory and nonrotatory.
2. The only time the force of a muscle and the force of gravity are not subdivided is when the angle of pull is 90 degrees.
3. Whenever the angle of pull of a muscle differs from 90 degrees, much of the force produced may go into the "undesired" action (nonrotatory component) of stabilizing the joint and the rest to the desired action of producing torque (rotatory component).
4. Whenever the angle of pull of gravity (resistance) differs from 90 degrees, much of the force produced may go into the undesired action (nonrotatory component) of dislocating the joint and the rest to the desired action of producing torque (rotatory component).

RATIONALE:

For example, when a resistance causes movement at a joint, as in the case of a heavy weight's causing the forearm to move from elbow flexion to elbow extension, not all of the force of the pull of gravity on the resistance produces elbow extension. The pull of gravity can also be subdivided into a rotatory and nonrotatory component. The former component pulls the forearm into a position of complete extension. The latter component serves to bring about instability (dislocation) of the joint.

The following diagram summarizes the factors involved in the production of torque at the joints.

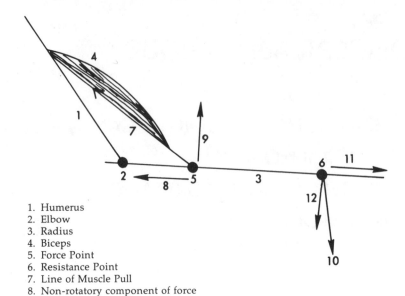

1. Humerus
2. Elbow
3. Radius
4. Biceps
5. Force Point
6. Resistance Point
7. Line of Muscle Pull
8. Non-rotatory component of force
9. Rotatory component of force
10. Line of resistance pull
11. Non-rotatory component of resistance
12. Rotatory component of resistance

ACTIVITIES:

1. Complete the following table.

	I F	II FA	III Product F × FA (Ft.-lbs.)	IV TFA	V Product F×TFA*	VI Difference III − V²**
A	100	1″	8.33	½″	4.17 ft.-lbs.	4.16
B	100	2″	_____	1″	_____	_____
C	200	2″	_____	½″	_____	_____
D	150	1″	_____	1″	_____	_____
E	50	2″	_____	¼″	_____	_____

_____

*Torque available to cause motion.

**Force used for some other purpose.

2. Questions regarding activity 1.

   a. What is another term for the torque represented in column V?

   b. What term applies to the force represented in column VI?

   c. What must be the angle of pull of the biceps on the radius in situation D in the chart above?

CONCEPT 47: TORQUE

NONROTATORY COMPONENTS OF MUSCLE FORCE (PULL) AND RESISTANCE YIELD "UNDESIRED" ACTIONS

INFORMATION:

1. Concepts 39 and 46 explain that a force can be subdivided into components. In human mechanics, the force produced by a contracting muscle and by resistance (gravity) can be subdivided into *rotatory* and *nonrotatory components.*
2. The purpose of the rotatory components of muscle pull and of the resistance is to produce motion at the joints.
3. The nonrotatory component of resistance attempts to dislocate the joint.
4. The nonrotatory component of muscle pull stabilizes the joint.

RATIONALE:

A person who hangs by his hands with his arms extended from a chin-up bar for any length of time feels pain in his elbows. The ulna and the humerus feel as if they were being pulled apart. The explanation lies in the fact that the elbow is no longer extending under the influence of gravity, and all of the force of gravity is nonrotatory and is attempting to dislocate the elbow joint.

When a person attempts to flex the elbow while the hands hold a heavy weight, he finds that the task is difficult because the force of the elbow flexors is subdivided. The nonrotatory component is used to stabilize the elbow joint against the effect of the nonrotatory component of gravity which seeks to dislocate the elbow.

Stability of many of the joints of the human body is as much a result of muscle pull as it is a result of ligamentous support. Specifically, it is the nonrotatory component of muscle pull that contributes to joint stability.

109

ACTIVITIES:

1. (Refer to activity 1, Concept 46).
   a. What is the purpose of the force listed in column VI?

   b. If activity 1 calculated the effects of gravity rather than muscle pull, what would be the purpose of the torque listed in column VI?

2. Concept 11 discusses the differences between spurt muscles and shunt muscles.
   a. Do the spurt muscles or the shunt muscles have the greater nonrotatory component of force?
   b. Why are the spurt muscles capable of moving joints with greater speed than the shunt muscles?

CONCEPT 48: TORQUE

THE ANGLE OF MUSCLE PULL CHANGES AS JOINT MOVEMENT OCCURS

INFORMATION:

1. The *angle of pull* of a muscle is the angle formed between the plane of the bone and the *line of pull of the muscle,* which lies along the long axis of the muscle.

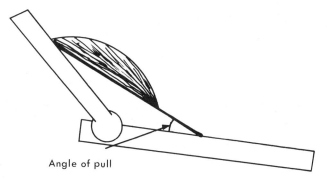

Angle of pull

2. When the angle of pull of a muscle on a bone is 90 degrees, all of the force of the contracting muscle is rotatory and is useful in producing torque at the joint. At any other angle a portion of the muscle pull is nonrotatory. As the angle deviates from 90 degrees (in either direction), the rotatory component decreases and the nonrotatory component increases. At an angle of pull of 45 degrees, the force is equally divided between the two components.
3. Movements of bones which articulate at joints produce changes in the angle of pull of the muscles producing the movement.

RATIONALE:

When motion occurs at a joint, the bones which articulate to form that joint change their relative positions. As the bones travel through their allotted range of motion, the angle between these bones either increases or decreases in magnitude. Since the muscle(s) responsible for movement at the joint insert(s) into one of the articulating bones, any change in joint angle can result in a change in the angle of muscle pull.

ACTIVITIES:

1. Given: A   Bicipital groove of humerus
            B   Elbow joint
            C   Distal attachment of biceps on radius; angle ABC is the angle
                of elbow flexion. Angle ACB is the angle of pull of biceps.

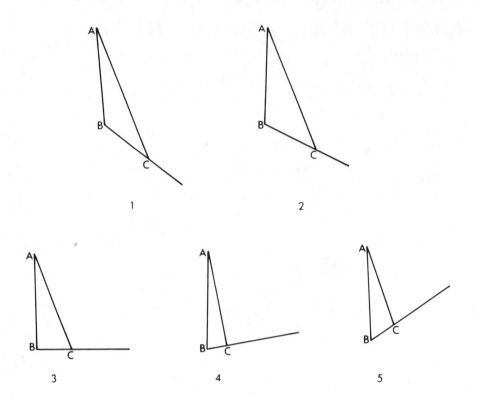

Use a protractor to measure the angle of elbow flexion (ABC) and angle
of muscle pull (ACB). Complete the following table.

Position	Angle of Flexion Angle ABC	Angle of Pull of Biceps Angle ACB
1		
2		
3		
4		
5		

2. Questions regarding activity 1.
   a. Which position provides for the greatest rotatory component of
      muscular force?
   b. Which position provides for the greatest nonrotatory component of
      muscular force?
   c. Which position most closely approximates the position in which the
      available muscle force is equally divided between rotatory and non-
      rotatory components?

CONCEPT 49: TORQUE

THE HUMAN BODY IS MECHANICALLY INEFFICIENT

INFORMATION:

1. In mechanical terms, efficiency is expressed as the ratio of work output divided by work input (energy expended). The per cent of efficiency is found by multiplying this decimal by 100. An inefficient machine is one which yields a low return of useful work in relation to the energy expended.
2. A third-class lever is an inefficient piece of machinery. A review of Concept 35 reveals that a loss of force occurs when third-class levers are used. This is due to the fact that the true force arm in a third-class lever is shorter than the true resistance arm.
3. When the angle of pull of a muscle is small, most of the force produced by the muscle is nonrotatory and is not useful in producing motion at the involved joint. (See Concept 46.)

RATIONALE:

The human body is mechanically inefficient because most of the joints in the body act as third-class levers with the force point close to the axis of motion. The result is a very short force arm in comparison to the length of the resistance arm. The muscles must generate great amounts of pull in order to move relatively light resistances.

The mechanical inefficiency of the body is compounded by the small angle of pull of the muscle on the bone. Only when the angle of pull is 90 degrees is the total pull of the muscle effective in moving the bone. Seldom does the angle of pull of muscle approach 90 degrees. A nonrotatory component of force is usually present, and only a portion of the pull of the muscle is useful in providing motion at the joint. (See Concept 48.)

ACTIVITIES:

1. Torque through elbow flexion and extension is represented below. To simplify matters, only the biceps muscle will be considered. Let us assume that a weight of 50 lbs. in the hand increases the total weight of the forearm to 55 lbs. The angle of pull of the biceps at this point in the range of

motion is 45 degrees. (Use a ruler to aid in answering the following questions.)

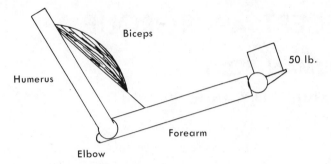

a. What is the length of the force arm?
b. What is the length of the true force arm?
c. What is the length of the resistance arm?
d. What is the length of the true resistance arm?
e. How many foot-pounds of torque are exerted by the resistance?
f. What force produced the torque in question e?
g. In order to maintain the resistance in its present position, how many pounds of force must the biceps produce (F×TFA = R×TRA)?
h. Explain the answers to question g in terms of angle of muscle pull.

i. Which class of lever is in effect at the elbow?
j. Why is there a loss of force in this class of lever?

k. What two reasons for the mechanical inefficiency of the human machinery are illustrated by activity 1?
   (1)
   (2)

CONCEPT 50: TORQUE

THE BEHAVIOR OF LEVERS CAN BE EXPLAINED IN TERMS OF MOMENT OF FORCE AND MOMENT OF INERTIA

INFORMATION:

1. Useful concepts in body mechanics are those of *moment of force and moment of inertia.*
2. The moment of force is the product of the amount of force multiplied by the perpendicular distance from the axis of motion (joint) to the distal end of the involved body part.
3. Since a motor act frequently involves the action of more than one joint, several moments of force can be involved in a skill such as batting.
4. The moment of inertia is the product of the amount of resistance multiplied by the perpendicular distance from the distal end of the lever to the axis of motion.
5. The concepts of moment of force and moment of inertia are "two-way street" concepts. These concepts can be used in describing the force exerted by the distal end of a lever (moment of force) or in describing the resistance to motion at the distal end of a lever (moment of inertia).

RATIONALE:

The moment of force is another method of illustrating the behavior of levers. Muscles apply their force on a bony segment (lever) at a point near the joint and the lever begins to move. The distal end of the moving segment develops velocity. The longer the bony segment, the greater its velocity. Therefore, the longer the distance involved in a moment of force, the greater the linear velocity at the distal end.

The concept of moment of inertia is useful in explaining why certain resistances are difficult to overcome. This is especially true when the resistance is encountered at the end of a body segment. An example would be lifting a light resistance on the end of a long pole. The light resistance is transmitted a long distance to reach the glenohumeral joint. The task would be much easier if a shorter lever (arm plus pole) were employed because the distance involved in the moment of inertia would be shortened.

115

ACTIVITIES:

1. The stick figure represents a bowler. Draw the moments of force from the following axes of motion: right hip, vertebral column, and glenohumeral joint (flexion).

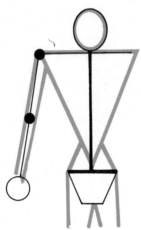

2. The following figures represent different patterns of throwing a baseball. Draw the moments of force for vertebral column rotation. (Note: The axis of rotation can be extended upward or downward.)

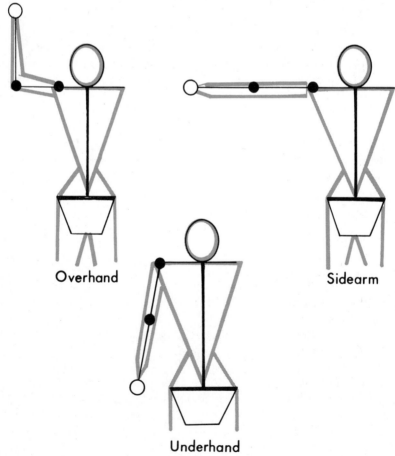

Overhand

Sidearm

Underhand

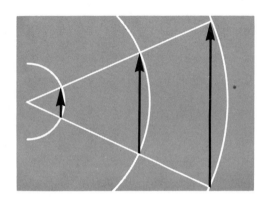

MOTION

CONCEPT 51: The human body exhibits two types of motion—translatory (linear) and angular.

CONCEPT 52: Human locomotion is translatory motion resulting from angular motion at the force-producing joints.

CONCEPT 53: A joint exhibits angular motion, while the distal end of a limb may exhibit angular and/or linear motion, yielding a given velocity.

CONCEPT 54: A greater linear velocity exists at the distal end of a longer lever.

CONCEPT 51: MOTION

THE HUMAN BODY EXHIBITS TWO TYPES OF MOTION — TRANSLATORY (LINEAR) AND ANGULAR

INFORMATION:

1. *Motion* is defined as a change of position.
2. *Translatory motion* occurs when the body is moved from one location to another.
3. Translatory motion, commonly called linear motion, occurs in two forms. *Rectilinear* motion refers to the body moving in a straight line, while *curvilinear* motion refers to the body following a curved, but not necessarily circular, path or moving around an axis which is not within the mass of the object (earth oribiting around the sun).
4. The second form of motion, *angular*, occurs when a body or object rotates around a fixed axis which is within the mass of the object (earth revolving around its axis). If the object is a lever, the distal end describes an arc or a complete circle.

RATIONALE:

The human body is often in motion in a straight line. Examples could include a base runner going from homeplate to first base, a person waterskiing behind a boat which tows him in a straight path, or a child sliding down a slope. These illustrate the form of translatory motion called rectilinear.

Sometimes the body exhibits the form of translatory motion known as curvilinear. Examples could include running around a curve on a quarter-mile track and a skier navigating the gates of a slalom course.

Seldom does the entire body exhibit angular motion. This would occur only when the body rotates around a fixed axis, as in the performance of a giant swing on the horizontal bar. A somersault dive incorporates both angular and translatory motion. The somersault depicts angular motion; whereas the path followed by the body mass as it descends to the water describes curvilinear motion. Angular motion occurs at the joints of the body when the distal end of the bony segment describes an arc as the proximal end rotates around a fixed axis, the joint.

119

ACTIVITIES:

Indicate with a check mark the type of motion occurring.

Action	Rectilinear	Curvilinear	Angular
Earth orbiting the sun		√	
Elbow flexion			
Running home from third			
Rounding a bend in track			
Free flight in ski jumping			
25 yard freestyle swim			
The approach in high jump			
The twist in a dive			
The path of a diver			
A "hook" in bowling			

CONCEPT 52: MOTION

HUMAN LOCOMOTION IS TRANSLATORY MOTION RESULTING FROM ANGULAR MOTION AT THE FORCE-PRODUCING JOINTS

INFORMATION:

1. *Locomotion* occurs when the moving object produces the force necessary for its motion.
2. *Translatory motion* involves moving in a straight line or a curved path.
3. *Angular motion* occurs around a fixed axis which is within the mass of the object.

RATIONALE:

The source of the force which results in human locomotion is muscular contraction. The muscles pull on the involved bones which, because of torque, pivot around a fixed axis called a joint. Specifically, during the production of power in the walk-run, certain muscles cause the hips to extend, the knees to extend, and the ankles to plantarflex. These joint actions are examples of angular motion with the joints serving as axes of motion and the distal end of the lever, the foot, describing an arc.

The net result is that the body as a whole progresses in a straight (rectilinear) or in a curved (curvilinear) path.

ACTIVITIES:

1. Complete the following table.

Action — Running Along a Straight Road

Type of motion _____

Subtype of motion _____

Force contributing _____

Joint Movements include:
Hip rotation, hip extension, knee extension, and ankle plantar flexion

Type of motion _____

2. Complete the following table.

Action — Running Around a Curve

Type of motion _____
Subtype of motion _____
Force contributing _____

Joint Movements
Hip rotation, hip extension, knee extension, foot inversion and eversion, and ankle plantar flexion

Type of motion _____

(Note: In activity 2, additional levers were employed. These produce the force which changes the path of the total body from rectilinear to curvilinear motion.)

CONCEPT 53: MOTION

A JOINT EXHIBITS ANGULAR MOTION WHILE THE DISTAL END OF A LIMB MAY EXHIBIT ANGULAR AND/OR LINEAR MOTION YIELDING A GIVEN VELOCITY

INFORMATION:

1. *Angular motion* occurs when a body segment rotates around a fixed axis. The distal end of such a segment describes an arc.
2. *Linear motion* is synonymous with translatory motion. (See Concept 52.)
3. *Angular velocity* can be measured at the axis of rotation and is expressed in units of degrees per second.
4. *Linear velocity* can be measured at the distal end of a moving body segment and is expressed in units of feet per second.

RATIONALE:

When a limb such as an arm moves, the proximal end of the humerus rotates within the glenoid fossa. Such motion occurs around a fixed axis, a joint, and is angular. The hand at the distal end of the moving limb may or may not be travelling in an arc; in either case, it would have linear velocity. The hand moves a certain number of feet in a certain number of seconds and may exhibit linear (translatory) motion. This fact can be demonstrated when an object such as a ball is released from the hand of a moving limb. The released ball does not orbit around the human body as it would if it possessed angular motion. Instead, the ball leaves the hand in a straight line, since the restraining force no longer exists.

An implement such as a racquet or paddle held in the hand of the moving limb also possesses linear velocity. This becomes evident when the student observes the behavior of a ball struck by a paddle. The ball leaves the striking surface in a straight line because of the law of inertia.

ACTIVITIES:

1. The following questions refer to a swinging pendulum.
   a. What type of motion occurs around the axis of the pendulum?

   b. Is it possible to make certain measurements and to calculate the linear velocity at the distal end?

   c. If the distal end of the pendulum struck a ball, what type of motion would be imparted to the ball upon impact?

2. During soccer activities, how can it be demonstrated that the foot possesses linear motion?

CONCEPT 54: MOTION

A GREATER LINEAR VELOCITY EXISTS AT THE DISTAL END OF A LONGER LEVER

INFORMATION:

1. If the force moving the levers remains constant, there is a direct relationship between the length of a lever and the linear velocity at the distal end.
2. *Linear velocity* can be determined by dividing the distance the distal end of the lever travels by the time expired ($v = d/t$).
3. The greatest linear velocity on a lever in motion exists at the distal end.
4. All moving segments of the human body are levers.
5. An implement held in the hand lengthens the arm as a lever.

RATIONALE:

Linear motion occurs at any point distal to the axis on a moving lever. The further any point is located from the axis, the greater that point's linear velocity. The maximum linear velocity for a moving lever occurs at the distal end.

When a lever is lengthened and the force moving the lever remains constant, the distal end of that longer lever travels around the circumference of a larger circle per unit of time. Thus, the linear velocity of the distal end increases. The opposite result would occur if a lever were shortened.

This concept is employed in many motor skills. The golfer who wishes to generate great linear velocity at the club head often selects a longer shafted club. The tennis player at the net who does not need to generate great linear velocity at the racquet face brings his elbow into his ribs, thus shortening the arm-racquet unit as a lever.

ACTIVITIES:

1. Given: An arm-racquet unit travelling through the motion of a forehand stroke in tennis.

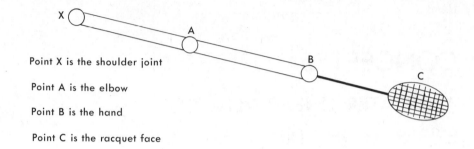

Point X is the shoulder joint

Point A is the elbow

Point B is the hand

Point C is the racquet face

a. Which point, A, B, or C, possesses the least linear velocity? Why?

b. Which point A, B, or C, possesses the greatest linear velocity? Why?

2. The following activities involve swinging a bat at a pitched softball.
   a. The batter swings a 32 inch bat. The striking surface of the bat travels 36 feet in three seconds. What is the linear velocity of the striking surface?

   b. Using the same amount of force, the batter swings a 36 inch bat of the same weight as in a. The striking surface of the longer bat travels 42 feet in three seconds. What is the linear velocity of the striking surface of this longer bat?

   c. If the batter wished to swing the 32 inch bat with the same linear velocity as the 36 inch bat, what would he have to provide?

MOMENTUM

CONCEPT 55: MOMENTUM

MOMENTUM IS THE PRODUCT OF THE MASS AND THE VELOCITY OF AN OBJECT

INFORMATION:

1. Momentum is the amount of motion possessed by a moving object.
2. Formulas for momentum:

Momentum = mass × velocity (Mo = mv)

$$\text{Mass} = \frac{\text{Weight}}{\text{Force of gravity}} \left(M = \frac{w}{32} \right)$$

$$\text{Linear Velocity} = \frac{\text{Distance}}{\text{Time}} \left(v = \frac{d}{t} \right)$$

RATIONALE:

The momentum of an object is the product of its mass multiplied by its velocity. Momentum may be changed by altering the mass of a moving object or its velocity.

The moving inertia of an object is proportional to its momentum. If two objects of equal mass travel at different velocities, the object possessing greater velocity is more difficult to stop. The same is true of two objects of unequal mass travelling with equal velocities; the heavier object is more difficult to stop.

ACTIVITIES:

1. Complete the following table by filling in the blank spaces concerning the momentum of four bowling balls.

Ball	Weight	Distance Travelled	Time	Momentum
A	10 lbs.	60 ft.	6 secs.	_____
B	12 lbs.	60 ft.	_____	4.50
C	14 lbs.	60 ft.	5 secs.	_____
D	16 lbs.	____	5 secs.	6.00

2. Questions concerning activity 1.
   a. What are the two factors which determined the momentum of the bowling balls?

   b. Why is the momentum of ball B less than that of ball D?

   c. Which ball would strike the pins with the greatest impact?

   d. Which ball would require the most effort for a "hook" ball?

CONCEPT 56: MOMENTUM

CHANGES IN MOMENTUM USUALLY OCCUR BECAUSE OF CHANGES IN VELOCITY RATHER THAN IN MASS

INFORMATION:

1. Momentum is directly proportional to mass and velocity. $M_o = mv$.
2. The following formula is also useful in solving momentum problems involving two colliding objects, provided one object comes to rest after the collision. The formula illustrates the law of conservation of momentum.

$$m_1 \cdot v_1 = m_2 \cdot v_2$$

3. The momentum of the first object equals the momentum of the second object.

RATIONALE:

Performers in motor activities seldom alter their own masses or the mass of an implement. To increase momentum, performers increase their own velocity or that of an implement such as a racquet.

The linebacker who wishes to increase his momentum to stop a ball carrier simply increases his velocity. The tennis player who wishes to hit a hard smash swings the racquet with greater velocity.

ACTIVITIES:

1. A 192 pound linebacker is running at a velocity of 10 feet per second. To what velocity must he accelerate in order to knock down a 224 pound fullback running at a velocity of 20 feet per second? ($m_1 \cdot v_1 = m_2 \cdot v_2$).
2. How fast must a 6 ounce softball travel to possess momentum equal to that of a 16 pound shot-put which moves at a velocity of 36 feet per second?

CONCEPT 57: MOMENTUM

MOMENTUM AT THE END OF A LONG LEVER IS GREATER THAN AT THE END OF A SHORT LEVER

INFORMATION:

1. The *linear velocity* at the distal end of a lever is directly proportional to its length, provided the force moving the levers remains constant.
2. Velocity is a component of *momentum* ($M_o = mv$).
3. *Momentum* can be transferred from a moving lever to an external object.
4. It takes additional force to move a longer lever with the same *angular velocity* as a shorter lever.

RATIONALE:

If it can be assumed that the angles of all clubheads are identical, then a golfer who makes good contact with a ball can hit the ball further using a 5 iron than a 9 iron. The explanation lies in the additional length of the 5 iron, which acts as a lever in the golf stroke.

Hitting with a 5 iron produces greater linear velocity than does hitting with a 9 iron (provided the muscular force swinging the irons is constant). The distal end of the 5 iron, therefore, possesses greater momentum, which can be transferred to the ball at the moment of impact.

The 9 iron, being a shorter lever, moves with a greater angular velocity than does the 5 iron. In order to swing the 5 iron with angular velocity equal to that of the shorter iron, the golfer must apply additional force.

ACTIVITIES:

1. Batter A goes to home plate with a 35 inch bat. Batter B selects a 40 inch bat. The batters apply equal forces when swinging these bats.
   a. Why could Batter B hit the ball a greater distance when he made contact?

133

b. Why would Batter B probably have a high ratio of strike outs to times at bat?

c. Which batter is likely to possess the greater strength?

2. One reason that a driver will send a golf ball farther than a 3 iron is that it possesses greater mass. What is the other reason?

3. A longer legged man has thigh muscle strength equal to that of a shorter legged man. Which man can kick a ball farther and why?

CONCEPT 58: MOMENTUM

MOTOR ACTIVITIES INCORPORATE THE PRINCIPLE OF TRANSFER OF MOMENTUM

INFORMATION:

1. The principle of transfer of momentum states that the human body is frequently put into motion by transferring momentum from a part of the body to the total body mass.
2. The same principle can apply to a ball which is put into motion by transfer of momentum from an implement.

RATIONALE:

In performing the standing broad jump, the subject adds to the performance by flexing the arms at the glenohumeral joint at the moment of take-off. Momentum is transferred from the forward swinging arms to the body. The same movement is employed in some styles of the racing start in swimming. The momentum of a swinging golf club is transferred to a stationary golf ball. The velocity of the ball is increased from zero to great velocity.

The formula $m_1 \cdot v_1 = m_2 \cdot v_2$ is useful in solving transfer of momentum problems. (See Concept 56.) If the mass and velocity of the body part or the implement are known, in addition to the mass of the body or the ball, then v_2, the velocity of the body or ball, can be calculated.

ACTIVITIES:

1. The arms of a standing broad jumper weigh 24 pounds and move forward with a linear velocity of 15 feet per second at the moment of take-off. The performer weighs 160 pounds. What portion of his velocity at takeoff will be due to transfer of momentum from the arms?

135

2. The kicking leg of an athlete weighs 24 pounds and moves with a linear velocity of 50 feet per second at the moment of contact with a three pound ball. If transfer of momentum is perfect and the leg comes to rest after contact, what will be the velocity with which the ball leaves the foot?

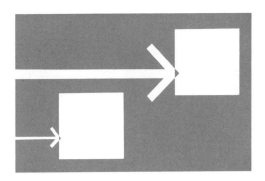

NEWTON'S LAWS OF MOTION

CONCEPT 59: Inertia concerns bodies at rest and bodies in motion.

CONCEPT 60: Inertia is directly proportional to mass.

CONCEPT 61: A force is necessary in order to overcome inertia.

CONCEPT 62: The greater the mass of an object, the greater the force needed for acceleration.

CONCEPT 63: If two forces of different magnitudes are applied to objects of equal mass, the greater force will provide the greater acceleration.

CONCEPT 64: The effect of a performer's action against the earth is nonobservable.

CONCEPT 65: The principle of action-reaction helps in identifying the force which propels the human body during locomotion.

CONCEPT 59: NEWTON'S FIRST LAW

INERTIA CONCERNS BODIES AT REST AND BODIES IN MOTION

INFORMATION:

1. Newton's first law states that an object tends to remain at rest or in uniform motion unless compelled by some outside force to change that state.
2. An object possesses *inertia* when at rest.
3. An object possesses *inertia* while in motion.

RATIONALE:

An object at rest possesses *inertia*. It will remain at rest until some force compels it to go into motion.

An object in motion possesses *inertia*. It will remain in motion in a straight line until some force compels it (1) to change velocity, (2) to change direction, or (3) to stop.

ACTIVITIES:

Complete the following table for each action by placing an X in the proper column.

Action	Resting Inertia	Moving Inertia
Person at military attention	_____	_____
Person dropping to a trampoline bed	_____	_____
Shot-put in mid-air	_____	_____
Diver leaving springboard	_____	_____
Sprinter at "take your mark!"	_____	_____
Baseball during the wind-up	_____	_____

Action	Resting Inertia	Moving Inertia
Rolling ball	_____	_____
Ball contacting bowling pins	_____	_____
Ball leaving swinging bat	_____	_____
Wrestler who is pinned	_____	_____

CONCEPT 60: NEWTON'S FIRST LAW

INERTIA IS DIRECTLY PROPORTIONAL TO MASS

INFORMATION:

1. *Inertia* is the tendency of an object to remain at rest or in uniform motion in a straight line.
2. An object at rest and an object in motion possess inertia. (See Concept 59.)
3. Inertia is directly proportional to the force causing the object to remain at rest or to move.
4. *Mass* is calculated by dividing an object's weight by 32, a constant figure for the pull of gravity.
5. Momentum is the quantity of motion possessed by a moving object, is calculated by multiplying the object's mass by its velocity, and is expressed as $(M_0 = mv)$ with $\left(\text{velocity} = \dfrac{\text{distance}}{\text{time}}\right)$.

RATIONALE:

A heavier object possessing heavier mass is subject to a greater pull by gravity and thus possesses greater inertia. The heavier mass requires a greater force to overcome its greater inertia and to put it into motion.

Since momentum = *mv, if velocities are equal,* a heavier mass possesses greater momentum and will require a greater force (1) to change its velocity, (2) to change its direction, or (3) to cause it to stop.

ACTIVITIES:

1. Calculate the number of foot-pounds of work necessary to cause motion in the following resting subjects. $(W = F \times D)$. Given: The coefficient of starting friction is 1.00.

Object	Weight	The Object Must be Moved	Work Required to Move
A	100 lbs.	2 ft.	_____
B	125 lbs.	3 ft.	_____
C	150 lbs.	4 ft.	_____
D	175 lbs.	5 ft.	_____

2. Calculate the momentum of the following objects in motion. ($M_o = m \times v$).

$$\text{Mass} = \frac{\text{weight}}{32}$$

Object	Weight	Velocity	Momentum
A	2000 lbs.	88 ft./sec.	_____
B	2500 lbs.	66 ft./sec.	_____
C	3000 lbs.	44 ft./sec.	_____
D	4000 lbs.	33 ft./sec.	_____

a. Which object would require the greatest force in order to cause a change in direction?

b. Which object would do the least damage upon collision?

c. Why does the heaviest object not possess the greatest momentum?

d. Why does the lightest object possesses the greatest momentum?

CONCEPT 61: NEWTON'S FIRST LAW

A FORCE IS NECESSARY IN ORDER TO OVERCOME INERTIA

INFORMATION:

1. A *force* may be defined as a push or pull.
2. A force is necessary in order to put an object in motion, change the rate of motion, change the direction of motion, or stop motion.
3. The force must exceed the inertia of the object at rest (mass) or the inertia of an object in motion (mv).

RATIONALE:

If a body is at rest, it will not go into motion unless a force is applied. That force must be sufficient to overcome the inertia of the object. (See Concept 60.)

If a body is in motion, it will not change its velocity, change its direction of motion, or stop moving unless a force is applied. That force must be greater than the momentum possessed by the object in motion.

ACTIVITIES:

Complete the following table by identifying the force responsible for the listed changes in inertia.

Change	Force Responsible
Boy falls into swimming pool	_____
Girl propels a bowling ball	_____
Rolling ball hooks to right	_____
Bowling pin falls down	_____
Diver changes direction at end of hurdle	_____

143

Change	Force Responsible
Trampolinist contacting mat changes direction	_____
A sprinter accelerates	_____
Released shot-put falls to earth	_____

CONCEPT 62: NEWTON'S SECOND LAW

THE GREATER THE MASS OF AN OBJECT, THE GREATER THE FORCE NEEDED FOR ACCELERATION

INFORMATION:

1. Newton's second law states that the *acceleration* achieved by a mass is directly proportional to the force applied.
2. A force is necessary to change the velocity of an object, either positively or negatively.
3. Acceleration is the rate of change of velocity. It may be expressed as positive acceleration or negative acceleration.
4. Acceleration is expressed algebraically as $\left(a = \dfrac{vf - vi}{t}\right)$ where a = acceleration, vf = final velocity, vi = initial velocity, and t = time (the length of the acceleration period). Acceleration is expressed in units of miles per hour per second or in feet per second per second.
5. Force is mass times acceleration (F = ma).

RATIONALE:

If two objects of differing masses are influenced by equal forces, the lighter mass will be accelerated to a higher velocity than the heavier mass. A greater force is needed to impart the same acceleration to the heavier object. Should equal forces influence a 10 pound object and a 20 pound object, the 10 pound object would receive twice the acceleration of the 20 pound object.

ACTIVITIES:

1. An automobile accelerates from 20 to 50 miles per hour in 5 seconds. What is its rate of acceleration?

2. A runner moving at a velocity of 10 feet per second increases his velocity in a 2 second time interval to a rate of 20 feet per second. What is his rate of acceleration?

3. Complete the following table.

Force	Mass 1	Vi	Vf	Mass 2	Vi	Vf
100 lbs.	10 lbs.	10	20	20 lbs.	10	—
100 lbs.	____	10	20	50 lbs.	10	15
150 lbs.	10 lbs.	5	—	20 lbs.	5	7.5
150 lbs.	20 lbs.	5	10	____	5	6

CONCEPT 63: NEWTON'S SECOND LAW

IF TWO FORCES OF DIFFERENT MAGNITUDES ARE APPLIED TO OBJECTS OF EQUAL MASS, THE GREATER FORCE WILL PROVIDE THE GREATER ACCELERATION

INFORMATION:

1. Newton's second law states that the *acceleration* achieved by a mass is directly proportional to the force applied.
2. A force is necessary to cause *acceleration*. The greater the force applied to an object, the greater the resulting acceleration.

RATIONALE:

If two differing forces are exerted against objects of identical mass, the greater force will cause the greater acceleration. Should forces of 100 pounds and 200 pounds be exerted against two 10 pound objects, the 200 pound force would produce twice the acceleration of the 100 pound force.

ACTIVITIES:

Complete the following table. Use the information in problem 1 to solve problems 2 to 5. (See Concept 62 for the formulas for acceleration and force.)

	Force	Mass	Vi	Vf
1.	100 lbs.	10 lbs.	10	20
2.	200 lbs.	10 lbs.	10	—
3.	100 lbs.	20 lbs.	10	—
4.	___ lbs.	10 lbs.	20	80
5.	200 lbs.	10 lbs.	—	60

CONCEPT 64: NEWTON'S THIRD LAW

THE EFFECT OF A PERFORMER'S ACTION AGAINST THE EARTH IS NONOBSERVABLE

INFORMATION:

1. Newton's third law states that every action produces an equal and opposite reaction.
2. A force exerted against the earth should cause the earth to move.

RATIONALE:

A performer standing on any fixed surface becomes a part of the mass of the earth. When such a performer exerts a force against the surface, we observe the action of the performer. However, we do not see the result of any reaction on the part of the earth. Because of its immense mass, the earth does not move any observable distance in response to the action of the performer.

A performer who stands on a tumbling mat flexes his trunk, which moves downward. According to Newton's third law, his legs would be expected to rise by equal and opposite action to meet the descending trunk. The legs do not move because the feet are in contact with the earth, which is too massive for him to move. The earth moves infinitesimally, but this motion is too slight to be seen.

ACTIVITIES:

1. In performing a vertical jump test, the subject flexes his hips and his knees. He then forcefully extends the hips and knees and plantarflexes the ankles. His body rises vertically above the surface.
   a. What is the observable action on the part of the subject?

b. What is the force which produces this action?

c. Why is there no observable reaction on the part of the earth?

2. In performing a tumbling stunt, why is it easier to gain height from the surface of a small trampoline than from the surface of the floor?

CONCEPT 65: NEWTON'S THIRD LAW

THE PRINCIPLE OF ACTION-REACTION HELPS IN IDENTIFYING THE FORCE WHICH PROPELS THE HUMAN BODY DURING LOCOMOTION

INFORMATION:

1. Newton's third law reveals that an equal and opposite reaction occurs as the result of an action.
2. During human locomotion, three lever systems produce forces which are exerted against the surface. These levers are the hip and knee, through extension, and the ankle, through plantar flexion.
3. A force can be subdivided into components.

RATIONALE:

During locomotion, the muscles which extend the hip and the knee and which plantarflex the ankle, produce a force which flows downward and backward and is transmitted to the earth through the foot of the propelling leg. This force is an action. In order for locomotion to occur, a reaction must flow back from the earth. (See Concept 64.)

The reaction force provided by the earth flows upward and forward through the propelling leg and acts upon the center of gravity of the body. The upward component of reaction elevates the center of gravity and aids in keeping the body erect. The forward component of reaction propels the body horizontally across the surface and provides for forward progress during locomotion.

ACTIVITIES:

1. Place the following letters in the appropriate slots.

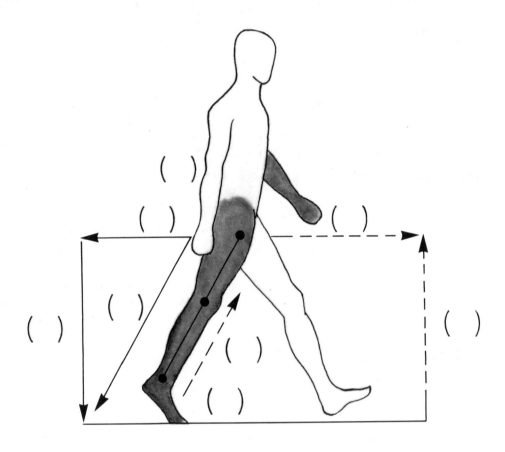

A. Propelling foot
B. Force generated by muscular contraction (action)
C. Vertical component of muscular force
D. Horizontal component of muscular force
E. Center of gravity of the body.
F. Reaction force coming from earth (reaction)
G. Vertical component of reaction
H. Horizontal component of reaction

2. In the preceding drawing, the center of gravity of the body would be subject to the pull of gravity.
    a. Which letter identifies a reaction which prevents the center of gravity from falling?
    b. Which letter identifies a reaction which propels the center of gravity horizontally forward?

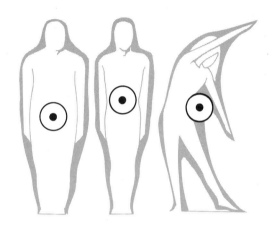

CENTER OF GRAVITY

CONCEPT 66: Determining the location of the center of gravity in the human body aids in our understanding of movement.

CONCEPT 67: Each human has a different specific location for his center of gravity.

CONCEPT 68: The location of the center of gravity of the body shifts when body parts move.

CONCEPT 69: The location of the center of gravity changes when external weights are added to the body.

CONCEPT 66: CENTER OF GRAVITY

DETERMINING THE LOCATION OF THE CENTER OF GRAVITY IN THE HUMAN BODY AIDS IN OUR UNDERSTANDING OF MOVEMENT

INFORMATION:

1. The *center of gravity* of the human body is an imaginary point in the center of the body where the weight of the body is balanced.
2. The force of gravity pulls upon the center of gravity.
3. The center of gravity serves as an axis of rotation for twists and somersaults when the body is airborne.

RATIONALE:

Gravity exerts a constant pull upon the human body. This fact is obvious when the body is airborne. For the purposes of mechanical analysis of motor skills, there is a reference point within the body where all of the body weight is centered. This reference point is known as the center of gravity. Its location may be plotted during the performance of motor activities.

The center of gravity is at the intersection of the three cardinal planes of the body. (See Concept 1.) This point is difficult to establish.

A rough estimate of the center of gravity in men is to locate it at 57 per cent of the standing height, measured from the feet. Since women tend to have a lower center of gravity than men, 55 per cent of their standing height is used. The above figures refer to a person in the anatomical position. Detailed methods of determining the location of the center of gravity may be found in leading kinesiology texts. (See Preface.)

ACTIVITIES:

1. Draw the three body planes in the drawing below and pinpoint the center of gravity.

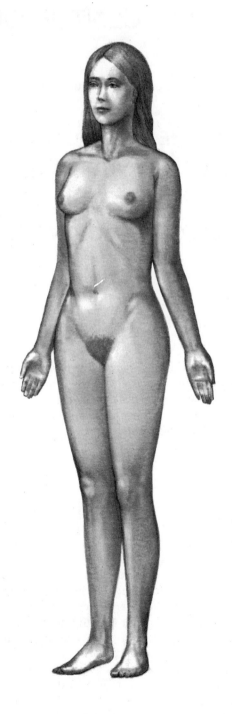

2. A male athlete stands 6 feet 2 inches tall. How far above his feet is his center of gravity?

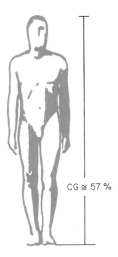

CG ≅ 57%

3. A female athlete stands 5 feet 4 inches tall. How far above her feet is her center of gravity?

CG ≅ 55%

CONCEPT 67: CENTER OF GRAVITY

EACH HUMAN HAS A DIFFERENT SPECIFIC LOCATION FOR HIS CENTER OF GRAVITY

INFORMATION:

1. Most methods used to locate the center of gravity in humans provide close approximations and can be described as "points which represent the location of the center of gravity."
2. The center of gravity can be defined as a point about which all the parts of the body will balance.
3. Humans vary slightly in the dimensions and masses of their body parts.
4. Amputations and congenital deformities affect the location of the center of gravity.

RATIONALE:

Every human varies slightly from his fellows in the dimensions and weights of his body parts. These are two factors which influence the location of the center of gravity. Each individual thus has a different central point about which different sized body parts would balance. Therefore, each individual possesses a distinct and separate location for his or her center of gravity.

ACTIVITIES:

Identify the approximate location of the center of gravity for each of the following figures. Drawing 1 is a standard model. The other drawings depict departures from that standard.

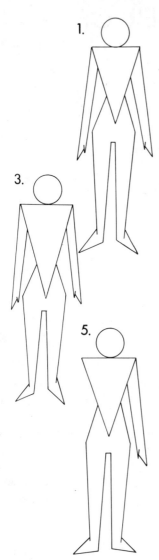

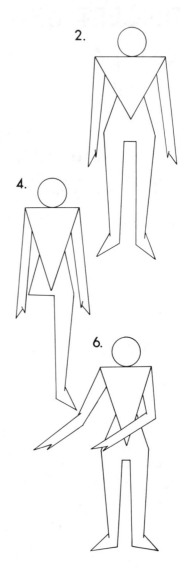

CONCEPT 68: CENTER OF GRAVITY

THE LOCATION OF THE CENTER OF GRAVITY OF THE BODY SHIFTS WHEN BODY PARTS MOVE

INFORMATION:

1. Human movement is described from the anatomical position. (See Concept 2.)
2. Methods are available to locate the center of gravity of a body while in the anatomical position. (See Concept 66.)
3. Performers depart from the anatomical position when engaged in motor skills.

RATIONALE:

Concepts 66 and 67 are concerned with the location of the center of gravity of a body in the anatomical position. Seldom is the body in the anatomical position during the performance of motor skills. Body parts constantly shift their position. Therefore, the points about which these body parts balance also shift. As a body part moves from the anatomical position, the location of the center of gravity shifts in the direction of that movement.

ACTIVITIES:

Identify the approximate location of the center of gravity in each of the following diagrams. Diagram 1 serves as a model. The other drawings depict postural changes from that model.

CONCEPT 69: CENTER OF GRAVITY

THE LOCATION OF THE CENTER OF GRAVITY CHANGES WHEN EXTERNAL WEIGHTS ARE ADDED TO THE BODY

INFORMATION:

1. When external weights are added to a body part, the distribution of the weight of the body is altered.
2. If a 150 pound individual lifts an object weighing 50 pounds, the total weight becomes 200 pounds and the center of gravity shifts in the direction of the 50 pound external weight.

RATIONALE:

Recalling that the center of gravity is the point about which all body segments balance, if an external weight is added to a body part, the weight of that body part changes. There must be a corresponding shift in the center of gravity in order to balance all body parts. The shift will be in the direction of the external weight. For example, external weights added to the ankles when running will cause a slight lowering of the center of gravity.

ACTIVITIES:

Answer the following questions.
1. Which way does the center of gravity shift when a bucket of water is carried in the right hand? (The right hand is in the anatomical position.)

2. An athlete swings a 35 pound weight around his body as in a hammer throw. What is the effect upon his center of gravity?

3. In question 3, what is the effect upon the stability of the body and why?

4. Native porters choose to carry heavy boxes on top of their heads rather than on one shoulder. Why? (Answer in terms of maintaining stability in the frontal plane.)

STABILITY

CONCEPT 70: The larger the base of support, the greater the stability.

CONCEPT 71: Raising or lowering the center of gravity within the base of support affects stability.

CONCEPT 72: Increasing the size of the base of support in the direction of an oncoming force increases stability.

CONCEPT 73: Stability and mobility are inversely related.

CONCEPT 70: STABILITY

THE LARGER THE BASE OF SUPPORT, THE GREATER THE STABILITY

INFORMATION:

1. The *base of support* involves the points of contact with the supporting surface and the two-dimensional area between these points of contact.

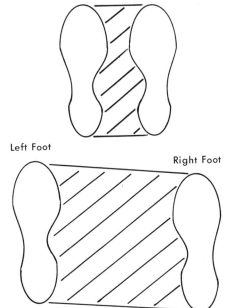

Left Foot

Right Foot

3. The *points of contact* are the body parts which touch the supporting surface. Examples would be the hands, feet, knees, or any combination thereof, including the total body.
4. When the center of gravity of the body moves outside any margin of the base of support, stability is lost.

RATIONALE:

A wrestler who is on his hands and knees is more stable than a wrestler who is on his feet. Since the margin of the base of support is further from the center of gravity in the former wrestler, it must be moved a greater distance to render this wrestler unstable. All other factors being equal, the larger the base of support, the greater the stability.

ACTIVITIES:

1. Drawn below are the bases of support for a football player in a two-point, a three-point, and a four-point stance. The dot represents the center of gravity. Draw in the bases of support.

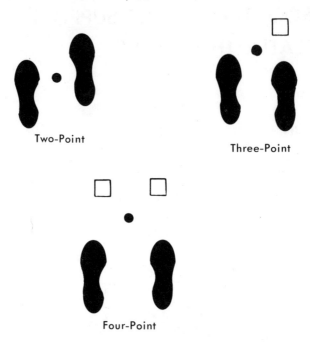

Two-Point

Three-Point

Four-Point

   a. Which drawing provides the largest base of support?
   b. In which drawing would the center of gravity have to be moved the greatest distance to go beyond any margin of the base of support?

2. In tumbling, why is the handstand a more difficult position to maintain than a head-and-hand stand?

3. An athlete suffered a knee injury. The doctor provided crutches so that the body weight would not be supported by the injured leg. The crutches provided a useful by-product of increased total body stability. How?

4. For each of the stances below, give an example of a different but specific sport activity.

   four-point position _____

   three-point position _____

   two-point position _____

   one-point position _____

CONCEPT 71: STABILITY

RAISING OR LOWERING THE CENTER OF GRAVITY WITHIN THE BASE OF SUPPORT AFFECTS STABILITY

INFORMATION:

1. Raising the location of the center of gravity within the *base of support* reduces *stability,* since the center of gravity must be moved a lesser distance to cause a loss of balance.
2. Lowering the center of gravity within the base of support increases stability, since the center of gravity must be moved a greater distance to cause a loss of balance.

RATIONALE:

Most athletes realize that they are more stable when they assume a semicrouched stance. The reason is that the athlete has lowered his center of gravity (hips) within his base of support.

Consider two men in separate canoes during windy weather. The first man stands up and his canoe capsizes. He raised the center of gravity of the man-canoe unit, which became unstable. The second man lies prone in his canoe and does not capsize. He lowered the center of gravity of the man-canoe unit and increased stability.

The higher the center of gravity, the less the body must tilt before the center of gravity goes beyond the margin of the base of support. The lower the center of gravity, the more the body must tilt before the center of gravity exceeds the base of support.

ACTIVITIES:

1. Consider the following drawings of a single block which has two possible centers of gravity, X and Y. In drawing A, the block rests on its base, and in drawing B the same block is tilted.

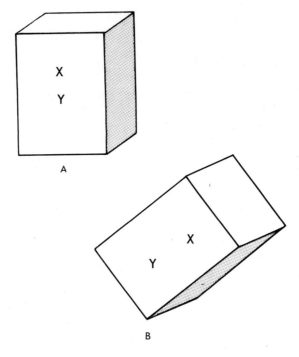

a. In drawing B, what would happen if Y were the center of gravity?

b. In drawing B, what would happen if X were the center of gravity?

c. Which position (X or Y) provides for the greater stability and why?

2. Why is it difficult to walk upon stilts?

3. Why is it safer to kneel in a canoe than to sit upon the seat?

CONCEPT 72: STABILITY

INCREASING THE SIZE OF THE BASE OF SUPPORT IN THE DIRECTION OF AN ONCOMING FORCE INCREASES STABILITY

INFORMATION:

1. The base of support can be extended in the direction of an oncoming force.
2. The center of gravity must be moved beyond any margin of the base of support in order to render a performer unstable.
3. If the center of gravity shifts toward the oncoming force while still within the base of support, stability is increased.
4. *Foot-pound* is defined as the amount of work accomplished when one pound of resistance is moved a distance of one foot.

RATIONALE:

A spotter is standing on the opposite side of a vaulting box from a springboard. Performers vault over the box. It is the duty of the spotter to prevent injury to any vaulter who crosses over the box out of control.

The spotter assumes a position with his feet spread in the *sagittal plane* as he faces the vaulters. He has widened his base of support in the direction of the oncoming force (the vaulter). His stability is increased because a vaulter would have to move the center of gravity of the spotter a greater distance to push it beyond the rear margin of the spotter's base of support.

The spotter may further increase his stability by leaning toward the vaulter. The spotter's center of gravity would now have to be pushed an even greater distance before he became unstable. It is interesting to note that the spotter adopts a crouched stance which lowers his center of gravity. This factor provides additional stability.

ACTIVITIES:

1. Given: The coefficient of friction between the feet of the catcher and the surface is 1.00. The catcher does not rotate backward during collisions.

a. A catcher blocking home plate has his center of gravity one foot from the rear margin of his base of support. The catcher weighs 200 pounds. How many foot-pounds of force are required to knock him down backwards?

_____ foot-pounds

b. Same as problem a, except that the catcher spreads his feet toward the oncoming runner so that his center of gravity is two feet from the rear margin of his base of support.

_____ foot-pounds

c. Same as problem b, except that the catcher leans toward the runner so that his center of gravity is now three feet from the rear margin of his base of support.

_____ foot-pounds

2. What additional movement on the part of the catcher will provide more stability?

CONCEPT 73: STABILITY

STABILITY AND MOBILITY ARE INVERSELY RELATED

INFORMATION:

1. A mass which is stable lacks *mobility* and is moved with difficulty.
2. A "stable mass" can be moved only when acted upon by a force.
3. Two forces which frequently cause the human body to move are muscular contraction and gravity.
4. A mass which is mobile usually lacks *stability*.

RATIONALE:

The more stable a mass, the more difficult it is to move. The more mobile a mass, the easier it is moved, and the less stable it becomes. Thus, these two factors demonstrate their inverse relationship.

Walking illustrates this concept. Before he moves, the subject is stable. Both feet are on the ground and his center of gravity is within his base of support. He lacks mobility. In order to move, the subject exerts a force against the ground with one of his feet or leans to "fall" off balance. Thus, his center of gravity moves forward over his front foot, going beyond the front margin of his base of support. The subject lacks stability but is now mobile. The subject recovers his former rear foot and places it on the ground in front of his center of gravity to prevent his falling off balance. Stability is momentarily re-established, and progress is momentarily restricted.

ACTIVITIES:

Answer the following questions concerning the standing broad jump.
1. In the preliminary position for this motor skill, does the body possess stability or mobility?

2. Before the performer's body can move, a force must propel his center of gravity beyond the front edge of his base of support. Identify this force.

173

3. At the height of his arc, what is the "visible" force affecting his center of gravity?

4. Upon landing, where is his center of gravity in reference to his base of support?

5. Why, upon landing, can his body no longer move to any extent?

SECTION THREE

APPLICATION

MUSCLES

CONCEPT 74: MUSCLES

TAUT HAMSTRINGS CAN LIMIT BODY FLEXIBILITY

INFORMATION:

1. The hamstring muscles have their upper attachment on the ischium at the lower rear portion of the pelvis.
2. If the hamstrings are taut, the pelvis is prevented from moving into a position of anterior tilt. During the "toe touching" exercise, if the pelvis cannot move into anterior tilt, the pelvis cannot be flexed completely over the heads of the femurs, and the performer may be unable to touch the toes.

RATIONALE:

Some tests of flexibility involve "toe touching" and "high kicking." Both these activities are dependent upon the ability to fully flex the femurs at the hip.

When a poor performance is observed, the investigator erroneously may attribute that poor performance to a lack of flexibility in the vertebral column. In reality, taut hamstrings may be the cause.

ACTIVITIES:

Execute the following tests for taut hamstrings.
1. Assume a supine position. Raise the right leg from the floor until it is vertical. Repeat, using the left leg.
2. Assume a sitting position on the floor with the knees completely extended. Place the feet against a wall so that the body will not slide forward. Reach forward *simultaneously* with both arms and touch the toes. Do not allow the knees to flex.
3. Go into a deep knee bend and place both hands on the floor, in front of the feet. Keeping the hands on the floor, attempt to elevate the hips until the knees are fully extended.

Each of these three activities is a screening test for taut hamstrings. Inability to perform these screening tests may indicate taut hamstrings.

CONCEPT 75: MUSCLES

THERE ARE THREE BASIC HAND POSITIONS USED TO PERFORM "CHIN-UPS"

INFORMATION:

1. The hands are in the *pronated* position when the palms face rearward in the anatomical position. (See Concept 2.)
2. The hands are in the *supinated* position when the palms face forward in the anatomical position.
3. The hands are in the *mid-position* when the palms face one another.
4. Review the attachments and functions of the elbow flexors. (See Concept 17.)

RATIONALE:

In many tests of physical fitness the performer is asked to execute chin-ups with the hands in the pronated position. There are valid reasons for requiring the pronated position.

When the hands are in the pronated position, the forearm is twisted so that the line of pull of the flexors is mechanically poor. The brachioradialis and biceps attempt to supinate as well as flex. For these reasons, the task is more difficult when the hands are pronated. It is the position of choice for climbing a rope ladder without the use of the feet and for scaling a wall. Performing chin-ups with pronated hands increases the ability to perform "real life" tasks.

ACTIVITIES:

Answer the following questions.
1. Which elbow flexor attaches to the ulna, and which does not move as hand position changes?

2. Which muscle makes the greatest contribution to elbow flexion when hands are pronated?
3. Why can the biceps make a greater contribution to elbow flexion when the hands are supinated?
4. Which hand position should be employed when the goal is to develop the biceps?
5. Why is the brachioradialis "exercised" in chin-ups? (See Concept 11.)

CONCEPT 76: MUSCLES

FOR EFFICIENT MOTOR ACTS, MUSCLES MUST POSSESS SUFFICIENT STRENGTH, ENDURANCE, AND FLEXIBILITY

INFORMATION:

1. *Muscle strength* is the capacity of a muscle to exert a pulling force to overcome a resistance one time. One pull-up represents the muscle strength factor for the upper extremities.
2. *Muscle endurance* is the capacity of a muscle to exert a pulling force to overcome a resistance over a given period of time. Two or more pull-ups represent the muscle endurance factor for the upper extremities.
3. *Muscle flexibility* is the capacity of a muscle to stretch or distend about the joints which it passes.

RATIONALE:

Physical educators and coaches have come to understand that the primary prerequisites for efficient human movement are muscular strength, endurance, and flexibility. Other factors such as neuromuscular speed, reaction time, and balance appear to develop later when learning motor skills.

Almost all motor acts demand that the individual possess a given degree of muscle development. Some activities place a premium on strength, others on muscular endurance, and many on muscular flexibility. Combatant activities demand a high level of strength development; long-lasting physical activities demand suffcent muscular endurance; whereas flexibility is specific to the activity or muscular group involved. The above understanding is consistent with the concept of specificity of muscle training.

181

ACTIVITIES:

Rank the factors below for each of the sport skills. (Note: 1 = most important, 2 = average importance, 3 = least important.)

Sport	*Strength*	*Endurance*	*Flexibility*
Gymnastics	1	3	2
Football			
Cross-country running			
Wrestling			
Tennis			
Track hurdling			
Soccer			
Distance swimming			
Shot-putting			

CONCEPT 77: MUSCLES

THE SPEED (VELOCITY) AT WHICH A MUSCLE SHORTENS IS INVERSELY RELATED TO FORCE (LOAD)

INFORMATION:

1. Physiologists have long since established the existence of the inverse relationship between speed of contraction (velocity) and force of contraction (load).
2. The greater the speed of contraction, the less force generated or load moved, and the greater the load, the less the velocity of shortening.
3. When no load (resistance) exists, a muscle's speed of contraction (velocity) is maximal; whereas when a load (resistance) is equal to or greater than the muscle's force, speed is zero.

RATIONALE:

When performing motor tasks which necessitate great demands upon the musculature, a decrease in the speed of contraction should be considered. When lifting heavy weights during muscle training, it is important to generate force over a longer period of time. For example, it is best to apply one's muscular force to a shot-put for an optimal length of time to ensure proper results.

When performing motor tasks when resistance is minimal, muscle mass may not be a prime consideration. It is the speed of contraction in a coordinated effort that is utmost in importance.

Thus, the understanding of this force-velocity relationship has significant implications in sport. For any one motor skill there is an optimal velocity in muscle action to ensure efficiency in human movement.

ACTIVITY:

Explain the following diagram.

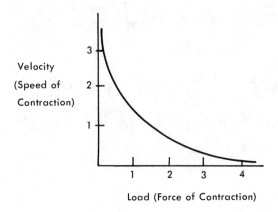

Load (Force of Contraction)

Describe:

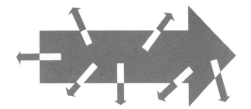

FORCE

CONCEPT 78: Force must be applied as much as possible in the direction of the intended motion in order to be effective.

CONCEPT 79: Effort which does not contribute to the desired result acts as a resistance.

CONCEPT 80: Centrifugal force (inertia) and centripetal force must counterbalance one another in motor activities.

CONCEPT 81: Gravity frequently counterbalances centrifugal force (inertia).

CONCEPT 78: FORCE

FORCE MUST BE APPLIED AS MUCH AS POSSIBLE IN THE DIRECTION OF THE INTENDED MOTION IN ORDER TO BE EFFECTIVE

INFORMATION:

1. A force can be subdivided into components. (See Concept 46.)
2. Force applied through the center of gravity causes an object to travel in a straight line.
3. It is not, however, our intent to minimize the importance of rotary motion, (see Concept 33.)

RATIONALE:

A right-handed golfer swings diagonally at a ball, and it travels down the fairway a short distance, landing in the right rough.

The explanation lies in the fact that not all of the force provided by the moving clubhead was applied in the intended direction, straight down the fairway. The diagonal swing caused the force of the clubhead to be divided into two components, forward and lateral. Since the ball moved laterally to the right, it could not travel as far forward as would be the case if all the force had been applied in the intended direction.

ACTIVITIES:

1. A person is pushing a heavy box across the floor. Muscular force is exerted in the direction indicated by the arrow.

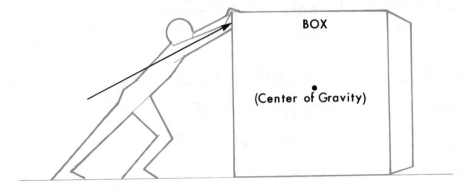

a. Draw dotted line arrows indicating the two components of force.
b. Which component represents unnecessary work and, in turn, increases the difficulty of the task?
c. Indicate by a solid line arrow the direction in which he should have applied his force.

2. A baseball pitcher who throws a curve ball supinates the forearm during the pitching motion in order to impart spin to the ball. In light of the information presented in this concept, why is it difficult for a pitcher to throw a curve ball with a velocity equal to that of a fast ball?

CONCEPT 79: FORCE

EFFORT WHICH DOES NOT CONTRIBUTE TO THE DESIRED RESULT ACTS AS A RESISTANCE

INFORMATION:

1. In the early stages of the learning of motor skills, performers are prone to make unnecessary movements which do not contribute to the desired result.
2. Such extra movements add to the workload, cause the performer to consume additional oxygen, and act as physiological resistance.

RATIONALE:

During imperfect performances of motor skills, inexperienced performers are apt to make unnecessary movements. Observe the thrashing of a beginning swimmer who attempts to stay afloat by performing the crawl stroke.

The problem of unnecessary movements in performing motor skills is not limited to the novice. Many runners employ movements which do little to produce locomotion. Examples include too high a leg lift and an overly long stride by the recovery leg. These unnecessary movements require additional energy expenditure and place increased demands on the oxygen delivery mechanism.

ACTIVITIES:

1. A swimmer was observed while practicing the crawl stroke kick. The lower leg rose above the surface on the upstroke, and the entire leg was submerged on the downstroke. Despite an exhaustive effort, the swimmer made little forward progress. Why?

2. Why is an overly vigorous arm action inefficient for the long distance runner?

3. Swimmer A used a few slow, powerful strokes when swimming underwater. Swimmer B employed a number of very rapid strokes but could not swim as far underwater as swimmer A. Explain.

CONCEPT 80: FORCE

CENTRIFUGAL FORCE (INERTIA) AND CENTRIPETAL FORCE MUST COUNTERBALANCE ONE ANOTHER IN MOTOR ACTIVITIES

INFORMATION:

1. Centrifugal force (inertia) attempts to pull an object out of its orbit. It is a force exerted away from an axis of rotation. (See Concept 32.)
2. *Centripetal force* attempts to maintain an object in an orbital path. It is a force exerted toward an axis of rotation.

RATIONALE:

During the hammer throw, centrifugal force (inertia) exerts a pull away from the axis of rotation (the athlete). The hammer attempts to escape from its orbit around the athlete. The source of centrifugal force is the mass of the hammer.

If centrifugal force is not counterbalanced by some equal and opposite force, the hammer escapes from its orbit and becomes subject to Newton's first law. In the hammer throw, the counterbalancing force is centripetal force, provided by the tensile strength of the cable of the hammer and by the muscular strength of the athlete.

Should the athlete flex his elbows, the amount of centripetal force would increase. Centripetal force would surpass centrifugal force, and the hammer would be drawn closer to the axis of rotation. Should centrifugal force exceed centripetal force, the athlete would be forced to release the hammer.

ACTIVITIES:

1. Complete the following table by supplying the source of centrifugal force and centripetal force for each activity and the involved axis of rotation.

Activity	Axis of Rotation	Source of Centripetal Force	Source of Centrifugal Force (Inertia)
Hammer throw	Trunk	Muscle contraction	Mass of the hammer
Lariat twirling			
Windmill softball pitch			
Giant swing			
Skater whirling on toe			

2. A boat describes a continuous circle of small diameter. A water-skier is attached to the boat by a tow line. (Note: answer each question as it relates to the skier.)
   a. What is the axis of rotation?
   b. What is the source of the centrifugal force?
   c. What is the source of the centripetal force?
   d. What will happen to the tow line if centrifugal force dominates?
   e. What path would the skier then follow?
   f. What would happen to the skier if centripetal force dominated?

CONCEPT 81: FORCE

GRAVITY FREQUENTLY COUNTERBALANCES CENTRIFUGAL FORCE (INERTIA)

INFORMATION:

1. *Centrifugal force* (inertia) must be counterbalanced during motor activities. (See Concept 80.)
2. Gravity can be employed to counterbalance centrifugal force.
3. The formula for banking a running track is expressed algebraically as $\left(\text{tangent } \theta = \dfrac{v^2}{gr}\right)$ with v = maximum velocity, $g = 32$, and r = radius of the circle.
4. The amount of centrifugal force generated in a motor activity is directly proportional to the velocity and inversely proportional to the radius of the orbit.

RATIONALE:

The smaller the radius of a track, the greater the centrifugal force (inertia) to which a runner is subjected. The athlete on a 1/12 mile track counter-balances centrifugal force by leaning inward. In this way, one employs gravity to offset centrifugal force.

The racing car maneuvers around a track of large diameter but does so at a high velocity. The greater the velocity, the greater the centrifugal force.

Tracks are banked in order to enable a runner or a car to employ gravity to counterbalance centrifugal force. The smaller the radius of the track or the greater the velocity developed, the greater the track is banked inwardly.

ACTIVITIES:

1. A runner traverses a curve on a track at a speed of 30 feet per second. The radius of the track is 29 feet to the inside edge. What is the angle of pitch of the track? (See formula above.)

2. In activity 1 above, if the width of the track is 8 feet, how high will the outer wall of the banking be?

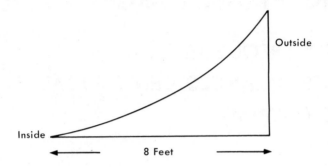

TORQUE

CONCEPT 82: The benefits of increased moments of force aid in understanding joint movement.

CONCEPT 83: The benefits of shortened moments of inertia aid in understanding joint movement.

CONCEPT 82: TORQUE

THE BENEFITS OF INCREASED MOMENTS OF FORCE AID IN UNDERSTANDING JOINT MOVEMENT

INFORMATION:

1. *Moment of force* was defined as the perpendicular distance from the axis of motion (joint) to the distal end of the moving body segment. (See Concept 50.)
2. The distal end of a longer lever possesses greater velocity than the distal end of a shorter lever if the force moving the levers is constant. Therefore, the longer the moment of force, the greater the linear velocity at the distal end. (See Concept 54.)

RATIONALE:

A ball can be struck more forcefully with a racquet held in the hand than if the palm of the hand were the striking surface. When an implement such as a tennis racquet is held in the hand, its length is added to the length of the arm. This results in an increase in the moment of force for each joint which helps to move the tennis racquet. The final result is an increase in linear velocity, since it is the racquet face, and not the hand, which strikes the ball.

ACTIVITIES:

1. The following stick drawing represents the arm travelling through a range of horizontal extension. Points A, B, and C represent the elbow, wrist, and finger tips.

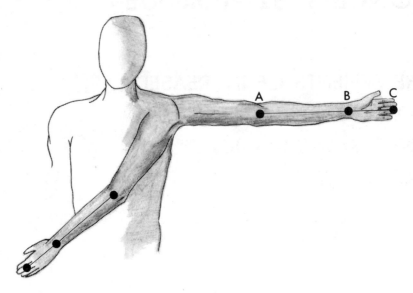

    a. Which point possesses the greatest velocity?

    b. Why?

2. Two softball bats are swung with equal force. Calculate the velocity of the tip of each bat. (Note: v = d/t.)

A	B
Length of bat = 30″	Length of bat = 42″
Length of arm + bat = 60″	Length of arm + bat = 72″
Distance bat tip travels = 9.5 feet	Distance bat tip travels = 13.5 feet
Time = .8 seconds	Time = 1.1 seconds
Velocity of bat tip = _____	Velocity of bat tip = _____

CONCEPT 83: TORQUE

THE BENEFITS OF SHORTENED MOMENTS OF INERTIA AID IN UNDERSTANDING JOINT MOVEMENT

INFORMATION:

1. Resistance, especially that produced by the pull of gravity, is capable of causing motion at joints.
2. A resistance is easier to move if it is located at the distal end of a shorter lever. (See Concept 50.)

RATIONALE:

When a person wishes to lift a heavy object, he moves his body as close as possible to that object. In this manner, he shortens the moment of inertia from the object to the joints providing the lifting motion. The downward pull of the resistance is transmitted across a shorter distance to the involved joints. The result is decreased downward torque. The lifting muscles must produce less force to overcome this decreased downward torque.

ACTIVITIES:

1. A golfer addresses a golf ball which is located 50 yards from the hole. Which of the following clubs should he select: 9 iron, 5 iron, or 3 iron? Why?

2. Why is it easier to raise a "stubborn window" by standing close to it?

3. A person wishes to raise a ten pound dumbbell by abducting the gleno-humeral joint. In the first attempt, the elbow is extended so that the moment of inertia is 3 feet. In the second attempt the elbow is flexed, re-sulting in a moment of inertia of 1.5 feet. What is the downward torque to be overcome by the deltoid in:
   a. the first trial: _____ foot-pounds
   b. the second trial: _____ foot-pounds

MOTION

CONCEPT 84: A diver can perform more somersaults in the tuck position, fewer in the pike position, and fewest in the layout position.

CONCEPT 85: A whirling figure skater employs changing moments of inertia to control angular velocity.

CONCEPT 86: Walking and running demonstrate the alternating action of the upper and lower limbs.

CONCEPT 87: Many motor activities involve the principle of continuity of motion.

CONCEPT 84: MOTION

A DIVER CAN PERFORM MORE SOMERSAULTS IN THE TUCK POSITION, FEWER IN THE PIKE POSITION, AND FEWEST IN THE LAYOUT POSITION

INFORMATION:

1. The *moment of inertia* is measured from the distal ends of the body to the axis of motion.
2. A moment of inertia is analogous to a lever. When the moment of inertia is lengthened, angular velocity decreases. The reverse is true when a moment of inertia is decreased.
3. The center of gravity of the body is the axis of motion for the total body during airborne somersaults. (See Concept 66.)

RATIONALE:

A diver performing front somersaults rotates forward in the sagittal plane around an axis of motion which passes through his center of gravity. The moment of inertia for this motor skill is measured from the center of gravity to the distal point of the body. The length of the moment of inertia is inversely proportional to its angular velocity (force remaining constant). The moment of inertia for somersaults is longest in the layout position, intermediate in the pike position, and shortest in the tuck position. The angular velocity is greatest in the tuck and least in the layout, with the pike occupying the intermediate ranking. Therefore, a diver can perform more revolutions per unit of time in the tuck, fewer in the pike position, and fewest in the layout position.

ACTIVITIES:

Complete the following table.

A diver is in the air for 2 seconds. His angular velocity for each of three body positions is stated. How many somersaults are possible? (360 degrees = one revolution.)
1 revolution).

Position	Length of Moment of Inertia	Angular Velocity	Somersaults Possible
Layout	3 ft.	180°/sec.	_____
Pike	2 ft.	_____	_____
Tuck	1 ft.	_____	_____

CONCEPT 85: MOTION

A WHIRLING FIGURE SKATER EMPLOYS CHANGING MOMENTS OF INERTIA TO CONTROL ANGULAR VELOCITY

INFORMATION:

1. As a figure skater whirls on the toe of one skate, the axis of rotation becomes the point in contact with the ice (the toe), and this axis extends vertically upward through the body.
2. The moment of inertia would be measured from the axis of rotation for the total body to the points of the body which protrude the greatest distance from the axis.

RATIONALE:

At a certain point in the routine, the figure skater balances on one toe and begins to pirouette on the toe of one skate, the opposite leg no longer contacting the surface of the ice. The speed of pirouettes (angular velocity) is slow at first, but as the skater adducts the free leg and the abducted arms, angular velocity increases at a rate difficult for the eyes to follow. To reduce angular velocity, the free leg moves away from the body, and the arms are abducted. Thus, the angular velocity is reduced to a rate where the skater can proceed to the next part of the routine.

Once the whirling action started, the skater produced no force which would explain the increase in angular velocity and the decrease that followed. The explanation lies in the change in the length of moments of inertia from the axis of rotation, the toe of her skate.

ACTIVITIES:

1. As the skater brought the free leg toward the midline and adducted the arms, what change occurred in the moment of inertia for the total body? Explain.

2. How did this affect the angular velocity around the toe of the skate contacting the ice? Explain.

3. As the skater abducted the arms and moved the free leg away from the midline as in an arabesque position, why did the angular velocity decrease? Explain.

CONCEPT 86: MOTION

WALKING AND RUNNING DEMONSTRATE THE ALTERNATING ACTION OF THE UPPER AND LOWER LIMBS

INFORMATION:

1. In human locomotion, the leg which pushes backward against the earth is the propelling leg. The leg which is swinging forward through space is the recovery leg.
2. The moment of inertia for the recovery leg lies perpendicularly between the hip joint and the sole of the foot.
3. The arm opposite the recovery foot swings forward via glenohumeral joint flexion and is flexed at the elbow.
4. The moment of inertia for the arms lies perpendicularly between the glenohumeral joint and the finger tips.
5. In both walking and running, the knee of the recovery leg flexes as that leg swings forward via hip flexion.

RATIONALE:

During running, the recovery leg moves forward in order to place that foot on the surface in a position under the center of gravity of the body. In order to time this recovery act properly, the forward swinging femur must possess considerable angular velocity. By flexing the knee, the distance from the hip joint to the sole of the foot is decreased. The result is a decrease in the moment of inertia for hip flexion. Thus, an accompanying increase in the angular velocity for hip flexion is realized.

For purposes of body balance, flexion at the hip in the recovery leg should be accompanied by flexion at the shoulder of the opposite arm. The elbow of that opposite arm moves forward in a flexed position, resulting in a decreased moment of inertia for shoulder flexion. An increase in angular velocity occurs, and the arms are able to match the velocity of the rapidly cycling legs.

ACTIVITIES:

1. The stick figure represents a person walking at a slow pace.

    a. What is the moment of inertia (in inches) for the recovery leg?

    b. What is the moment of inertia for the forward swinging opposite arm?

2. The following stick figure represents the same person running.

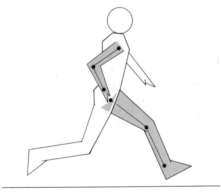

    a. What is the moment of inertia (in inches) for the recovery leg?

    b. What is the moment of inertia for the forward swinging opposite arm?

3. Why does the shoulder in the first figure possess less angular velocity than that in the second figure?

4. Why does the leg in the second figure possess greater angular velocity than that in the first figure?

5. Why would a person with a stiff knee experience difficulty in recovering that leg when running?

CONCEPT 87: MOTION

MANY MOTOR ACTIVITIES INVOLVE THE PRINCIPLE OF CONTINUITY OF MOTION

INFORMATION:

1. The principle of continuity of motion states that when a sequence of movements is employed in a motor skill, there should be no pause between them.
2. Motor activities demand that proper transfer of momentum be conducted so that desired outcomes are realized. (See Concept 58.)
3. *Efficiency* involves a high ratio between energy input and work accomplished.

RATIONALE:

A single motor skill may involve movement at several joints. Several levers, therefore, contribute to the production of force. If a pause occurs between the contribution of any two levers in the chain, the force and momentum generated in any preceding levers are reduced. The result is a reduction of force for the entire motor skill and an imperfect performance.

In serving a tennis ball, if a pause occurs between rotation of the vertebral column and movements of the humerus, some of the force produced by the vertebral column rotation is lost. The result is a weakly hit ball.

ACTIVITIES:

Write a brief explanation for each of the following mishaps.
a. A batter interrupts his swing between body rotation and arm extension. The result is a weakly hit ground ball.

b. A pitcher's foot slips on the pitcher's plate. Hip rotation ceases; then, body rotation begins. The pitched ball hits the ground in front of home plate.

c. A basketball player pauses between hip extension and elbow extension during the free throw. The ball does not reach the front rim of the basket.

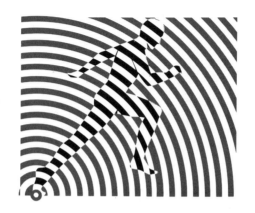

MOMENTUM

CONCEPT 88: In motor activities in which the body becomes airborne, transfer of momentum must occur at the instant of takeoff.

CONCEPT 89: During some motor activities, momentum is provided to the body via jumping, giving impetus to the body.

CONCEPT 90: Many motor activities require that a performer must reduce the momentum of an object receiving impetus.

CONCEPT 91: Many motor activities require that a performer provide momentum to an object, thereby giving impetus to an object.

CONCEPT 88: MOMENTUM

IN MOTOR ACTIVITIES IN WHICH THE BODY BECOMES AIRBORNE, TRANSFER OF MOMENTUM MUST OCCUR AT THE INSTANT OF TAKEOFF

INFORMATION:

1. The body is often put into motion by transfer of momentum from a part of the body to the total body mass. (See Concept 58.)
2. If transfer of momentum is attempted prior to takeoff, the momentum of the body part is dissipated before the body leaves the surface.
3. If transfer of momentum is attempted after the body is airborne, the body is subject to Newton's third law. (See Concept 94.)

RATIONALE:

In performing the standing broad jump, the performer may flex the arms too soon. If so, the momentum built up in the forward moving arms dissipates during the lag period before the body leaves the surface. The result is a poor performance. Sometimes a performer may wait until he is airborne to flex the arms. He is now subject to Newton's third law. As the arms swing forward and upward (action), the legs are forced downward and backward by reaction. The result is that the feet are placed in a disadvantageous landing position.

In order to contribute to performances, the transfer of momentum from arms to body must occur at the exact moment of takeoff.

213

ACTIVITIES:

Row I shows transer of momentum properly occurring just prior to take-off or contact in three motor activities.

Row II shows the same motion occurring after the performer leaves the surface in the same three motor activities. In Row II, indicate by arrows how transfer of momentum will affect the airborne body.

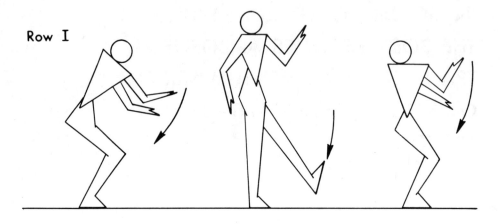

Row I

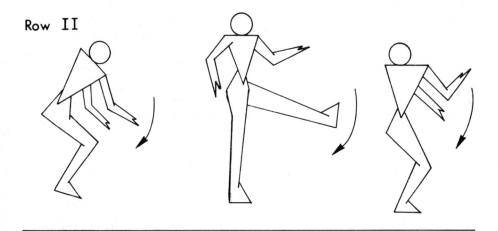

Row II

CONCEPT 89: MOMENTUM

DURING SOME MOTOR ACTIVITIES, MOMENTUM IS PROVIDED TO THE BODY VIA JUMPING (GIVING IMPETUS TO THE BODY)

INFORMATION:

1. Jumping, one of the basic forms of movement, is useful in several different sport activities; it consists of projecting the body into the air by contraction of the powerful leg muscles.
2. Jumping is initiated by one or both feet and involves landing on the ground with both feet.
3. Many motor activities include the same type of jump whether the purpose of the jump is distance or height.

RATIONALE:

Whether jumping for distance or height or from a stand, similar mechanical principles apply.

When distance is desired, speed under control is necessary. At the instant of takeoff, all desired force should be generated through a firm "takeoff foot." The arms are swung at the proper moment to utilize a transfer of momentum. The goal is to project the center of gravity of the individual as far forward as possible. If height while jumping is the goal, speed is not as important a factor. In this case, the center of gravity must be projected vertically.

Jumping from a standing position is basically the same as jumping for height; however, no prior linear movement is necessary for this skill.

ACTIVITIES:

List three specific skills in sport that utilize jumping for distance, jumping for height, and jumping from a standing position.

Distance	Height	Stand
Long jumping	High jumping	Basketball rebounding

CONCEPT 90: MOMENTUM

MANY MOTOR ACTIVITIES REQUIRE THAT A PERFORMER REDUCE THE MOMENTUM OF AN OBJECT, RECEIVING IMPETUS

INFORMATION:

1. Landing, one of the most fundamental skills performed in motor activities, demands proper execution of technique in order to avoid injury. Skills in acrobatic stunts and combative games are examples.
2. Catching external objects can be difficult, since a premium is placed upon the individual's motor and perceptual abilities.
3. Both landing and catching share similar mechanical applications, but one fundamental principle involved is that of dissipation of energy.

RATIONALE:

When performing on hard surfaces, landing may be aided by proper footwear, or, in the case of stunts and tumbling, by mats. The absorptive qualities of such equipment protect the body from injury. Some of the momentum of the body is dissipated in compacting the sole of the footwear and the mat.

Many mechanical factors are considered in the execution of catching techniques. The individual is asked to "give with the ball" to reduce its kinetic energy or is allowed to increase the absorbing surface by using a glove.

ACTIVITIES:

1. List four fundamental teaching principles for landing that would be given in the instruction of a gymnastic unit.

   a.

   b.

   c.

   d.

2. Compare and contrast the mechanical principles which would be used in receiving the impetus of a baseball with those used in receiving the impetus of an offensive ball carrier in football (see Concepts 71 and 72).

CONCEPT 91: MOMENTUM

MANY MOTOR ACTIVITIES REQUIRE THAT A PERFORMER PROVIDE MOMENTUM TO AN OBJECT, THEREBY GIVING IMPETUS TO AN OBJECT

INFORMATION:

1. Throwing and striking techniques are difficult skills to perform.
2. When throwing or striking an object for distance, maximum linear velocity of a long lever system with a proper angle of release is essential.
3. Application of force through the center of gravity of the object is necessary for desired outcomes.
4. A premium is placed upon the abilities of the perceptual qualities of the individual to respond with smoothly coordinated muscular effort.

RATIONALE:

To keep the ball on the fairway in golf, to throw a baseball accurately, to complete a touchdown pass in football, and to score the winning basket in basketball are all excellent examples of difficult motor skills employing basic mechanical principles. To execute these skills requires that the performer "feed" his central nervous system the correct information.

Some of the mechanical principles involved in striking a tennis ball accurately include perceiving the speed at which the ball is travelling, determining where the opponent is or will be, striking the ball through its center of gravity for proper speed or giving spin for proper placement, gripping the racquet firmly at impact, employing a stable base from which to strike, summing internal forces (muscles), utilizing a long lever for sufficent linear velocity, and executing a proper follow-through.

ACTIVITIES:

1. List three sport skills in which an overarm pattern of striking is employed.
    a.
    b.
    c.

2. List three sport skills, different from those in activity 1, in which a side-arm pattern is employed.
   a.
   b.
   c.
3. List three sport skills other than those in activities 1 and 2 in which an underarm pattern is employed.
   a.
   b.
   c.

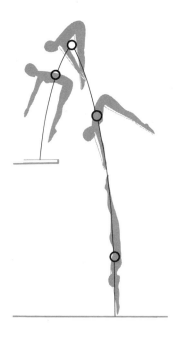

NEWTON'S LAWS

CONCEPT 92: The force which accelerates an object can be provided by an implement's giving impetus to an object.

CONCEPT 93: When the body is in free flight, no amount of maneuvering of body parts can alter the path of the center of gravity.

CONCEPT 94: The action-reaction principle is observable when the performer is airborne.

CONCEPT 95: One foot must be in contact with the surface when striking an object.

CONCEPT 92: NEWTON'S SECOND LAW

THE FORCE WHICH ACCELERATES AN OBJECT CAN BE PROVIDED BY AN IMPLEMENT'S GIVING IMPETUS TO AN OBJECT

INFORMATION:

1. Newton's second law specifies that a force is necessary to accelerate an object.
2. An implement in the hands lengthens the moment of force from any axis of motion to the distal end of a lever. (See Concept 50.)
3. Momentum = mass × velocity ($Mo = mv$).

RATIONALE:

Since an implement such as a bat or a racquet increases the length of the moment of force from any axis to the distal end of a lever, additional linear velocity is generated at the distal end of the implement. (See Concept 54.) The momentum ($Mo = mv$) of the implement is increased and serves as a force which can propel a ball at the moment of impact between implement and ball. The result is a change in the velocity of the ball (acceleration).

If the arm alone is swung with the same force as that arm holding a racquet, the arm with the racquet will provide greater acceleration to a ball which is contacted. The reason is that the racquet provides an increased moment of force for movements of the arm.

223

ACTIVITIES:

1. Explain why it is easier to hit a baseball farther than a softball. (Answer in terms of bat length.)

2. Why do you use a 1 wood club when hitting a golf ball for great distances and a 9 iron for short distances?

CONCEPT 93: NEWTON'S THIRD LAW

WHEN THE BODY IS IN FREE FLIGHT, NO AMOUNT OF MANEUVERING OF BODY PARTS CAN ALTER THE PATH OF THE CENTER OF GRAVITY

INFORMATION:

1. The body becomes a projectile during jumping, leaping, bouncing, and diving activities.
2. According to Newton's first law, a force is necessary in order to change the path of a body in motion.
3. A body which is airborne is free from surfaces against which it could exert a force.
4. The path of the human body in flight is predetermined at the instant of takeoff.
5. A body in flight is subject to Newton's third law of action-reaction.

RATIONALE:

The path of the center of gravity of the human body in flight is predetermined at the moment of takeoff by two factors: (1) the force exerted or the velocity obtained, and (2) the angle of takeoff. Once the body is airborne, it lacks a surface against which force can be applied. No amount of maneuvering of body parts can change the predetermined path of the center of gravity.

The body in flight is subject to Newton's law of action-reaction. Any movement made on one side of the center of gravity will cause body parts on the other side of the center of gravity to move in the opposite direction.

The running long jumper makes many movements in midair. These movements have no effect upon the path of his center of gravity.

225

ACTIVITIES:

The following series of stick figures represents movements performed by a long jumper while in midair. The arrows represent the movements initiated by the jumper (action). Indicate by arrows the opposite direction movements produced by reaction.

CONCEPT 94: NEWTON'S THIRD LAW

THE ACTION-REACTION PRINCIPLE IS OBSERVABLE WHEN THE PERFORMER IS AIRBORNE

INFORMATION:

1. According to Newton's third law every action of the human body should be accompanied by an equal and opposite reaction.
2. An action induced above the center of gravity of the body should produce a reaction below the center of gravity.
3. When a performer is in contact with the earth, there appears to be no opposite and equal reaction. The earth is too massive to be moved observably.

RATIONALE:

When a person is in midair and free from support, his body mass is obviously no longer affixed to the mass of the earth. During the airborne period, the law of action-reaction produces observable results. If the performer flexes his trunk (action), his thighs will rise toward his descending face (reaction).

ACTIVITIES:

1. An excellent way to demonstrate the principle of action-reaction is to stand on a stool which is capable of spin. Grab a baseball bat and try to perform the task of hitting an imaginary ball. What are the observable results? Explain.

2. A trampolinist, while airborne, extends his spine.
   a. Which way will his legs and feet move?

b. If he extends his spine while standing on the ground, why would his legs and feet not move?

3. A trampolinist, while airborne in a sitting pose, rotates his head and shoulders to the right.
   a. Which way will his legs move?
   b. If he performed this action while sitting on the ground, why would his legs not move?

CONCEPT 95: NEWTON'S THIRD LAW

ONE FOOT MUST BE IN CONTACT WITH THE SURFACE WHEN STRIKING AN OBJECT

INFORMATION:

1. Newton's third law reveals that every action produces an equal and opposite reaction.
2. The emphasis in this concept is on the words opposite reaction.
3. If one foot is in contact with the surface when forward impetus is given to an object (action), the body cannot be driven backward (reaction).

RATIONALE:

When the body is airborne at the instant a body part or an implement strikes an object, an ineffective action results because the body is subject to Newton's third law. If a foot swings forward to kick a ball while the body is in midair, the reaction at impact will drive the body backward. The reactive force from the ground which is necessary to propel the ball forward is absent, and the ball travels only a short distance.

However, when the body of the kicker is attached to the ground via the nonkicking leg, two events occur which add considerable distance to the kicked ball.

    a. The mass of the body-earth combination is too great to be driven backward (reaction) as the ball is kicked forward (action).

    b. The earth provides a reaction as the nonkicking leg pushes against the surface, and this reaction aids in propelling the ball.

ACTIVITIES:

Kicker A punts a football with the right foot, and the left foot is in contact with the earth. Kicker B punts a football with the right foot while the left foot is off the ground.

    a. Which kicker will produce the longest punt?

b. What will happen to the body of Kicker B as the kicked ball starts forward?

c. Why will the body of Kicker A not be affected in the same manner?

d. What are the two forces which account for the additional length of Kicker A's punt?

e. Which of these forces is not available to Kicker B?

f. Why is this second force not available to Kicker B?

FRICTION

CONCEPT 96: In the absence of friction, horizontal movement is impossible.

CONCEPT 97: The coefficient of sliding friction is less than that of starting friction.

CONCEPT 98: The starting positions for many motor skills demand sufficient friction.

CONCEPT 99: Running in sand or mud is difficult.

CONCEPT 96: FRICTION

IN THE ABSENCE OF FRICTION, HORIZONTAL MOVEMENT IS IMPOSSIBLE

INFORMATION:

1. *Friction* is the resistance to motion created by contact between two surfaces.
2. *Starting friction* is synonymous with stopping friction and is directly proportional to the amount of force holding an object against the surface.
3. Friction is directly proportional to the weight of an object.
4. Formulas.
   a. To determine the *force (F) needed to start an object moving:*
      $$F = kf$$
      k = coefficient of starting friction
      f = force holding the object against the surface (usually the weight of the object)
   b. To determine the *coefficient of starting friction:*
      $$K = \frac{F}{f}$$
      F = Force needed to start an object moving
      f = Force holding the object against the surface

RATIONALE:

During human locomotion and in the performance of motor skills, friction is the "glue" between the surface of the foot and the supporting surface. Friction insures that the supporting surface can push back against the foot with an equal and opposite reaction. The coefficient of friction is reduced when walking on an oily surface. When muscular force is applied to the foot, the foot slips backward. No equal and opposite reaction can occur from the surface, and no forward progress results.

ACTIVITIES:

1. An automobile which is motionless on an icy surface weighs 3000 pounds. A force of 1000 pounds applied to the car will cause it to move. What is the coefficient of starting friction of the icy surface?

2. The same automobile is parked in a dry asphalt lot. The coefficient of friction for this surface is 1.00. How much force must be applied to the auto before it will move?

CONCEPT 97: FRICTION

THE COEFFICIENT OF SLIDING FRICTION IS LESS THAN THAT OF STARTING FRICTION

INFORMATION:

1. The *coefficient of friction* in a sliding object is always less than that of an object which is stopping.
2. It is easier for an object to continue to slide on surfaces with low coefficients of friction than it is for it to stop.
3. *Sliding friction* is independent of the area in contact with the surface.
4. *Starting* and *stopping friction* are synonymous.

RATIONALE:

A car that begins to slide on an icy road continues to slide for a long distance if it remains on that icy road. The coefficient of friction for the icy surface is low, so the car continues sliding.

An athlete who begins to slide while running on a wet field will slide for some distance. For this reason football players often employ "mud cleats" on wet fields. Such cleats are longer than ordinary cleats and increase the coefficient of friction between the shoe and the mud.

It is the increased coefficient of friction caused by the longer cleat which reduces the chances of sliding and increases the ability to stop once sliding does begin.

Sliding friction is independent of the area of contact with the surface. If an athlete begins to slide on a surface, the size of the soles of his footwear makes no difference in his ability to stop. A wide-soled sneaker has no advantage over a narrow-soled sneaker.

ACTIVITIES:

1. A boy runs along a wintry sidewalk and deliberately begins to slide on his feet on an icy spot. Why can he not stop the sliding quickly?

2. During human locomotion, what component of force would have to be reduced in order to prevent the possibility of sliding on a slippery surface? (See Concept 65.)

3. A toy automobile is rolling down a small ramp. The front wheels become "locked" but the rear wheels are free to slide. The rear end of the car pivots around the front wheels and the car stops, rear end first, on the ramp. Explain the behavior of the wheels in terms of starting and stopping friction.

CONCEPT 98: FRICTION

THE STARTING POSITIONS FOR MANY MOTOR SKILLS DEMAND SUFFICIENT FRICTION

INFORMATION:

1. The coefficient of starting friction depends upon the nature and condition of the contacting surfaces.
2. Friction is lessened by surfaces which are smooth, is not appreciably altered by dry surfaces, but is reduced on well-oiled surfaces.

RATIONALE:

Track sprinters wear spikes; football players have cleats on their shoes; and the top surface of a diving board is covered with an abrasive substance. All of the above methods affect the condition of contacting surfaces. Rough surfaces increase the coefficient of starting friction. Abrasive surfaces on diving boards present a very rough surface to compensate for the wet feet of the diver. Treads on sneakers present a rough surface.

Spikes and cleats on footwear allow for considerable interlocking between the shoes and the surface. Interlocking increases the coefficient of starting friction.

ACTIVITIES:

1. Circle the letter of the examples which increase the coefficient of starting friction.
   a. Snowtread tires on automobiles
   b. Wax on a dance floor
   c. Abrasive surface on the starting block for swimming races
   d. Paint which contains sand applied to shower room floors
   e. Dancing slippers
   f. Spikes on golf shoes
   g. Starting holes dug in a track
   h. Soap on a shower room floor
2. What component of force or velocity is reduced when a decreased coefficient of starting friction exists for human locomotion? (See Concept 65.)

237

CONCEPT 99: FRICTION

RUNNING IN SAND OR MUD IS DIFFICULT

INFORMATION:

1. Friction is the "glue" between the surface and the foot which insures that an opposite and equal reaction from the surface will occur.
2. Sand, mud, snow, ice, and other slippery surfaces have low coefficients of friction. (See Concept 97.)

RATIONALE:

Sand, mud, snow, ice, and other slippery surfaces having low coefficients of friction cannot push back against the foot with an equal and opposite reaction. Therefore, locomotion is inefficient.

When the foot strikes in sand, some of the force of the foot is wasted in displacing the sand. Less force is available to cause an equal and opposite reaction from the earth.

The same situation exists when running in the mud. Some of the force transmitted by the foot is wasted in displacing the mud. In addition, mud has a low coefficient of friction, so the foot slips backward. A reduced equal and opposite reaction occurs, and no forward progress results. Ice and snow also have low coefficients of friction.

ACTIVITIES:

1. Why does sand placed on an icy surface increase the ease of locomotion?

2. Why do some coaches encourage athletes to train by running on sandy terrain?
   Note: The force which displaces the sand does not contribute to the desired result. (See Concept 79.)

3. Explain in terms of starting friction the value of chains on tires during winter driving.

4. When walking on slippery surfaces, why does an individual shorten the stride?

Note: When the foot strikes the surface, the foot is directly under the center of gravity of the body. This increases the vertical component of gravity. The force holding the foot against the slippery surface is increased. (See Concept 97.)

STABILITY

CONCEPT 100: There are motor activities in which the performer desires to maintain stability.

CONCEPT 101: There are some motor activities in which the performer wishes to lose stability.

CONCEPT 100: STABILITY

THERE ARE MOTOR ACTIVITIES IN WHICH THE PERFORMER DESIRES TO MAINTAIN STABILITY

INFORMATION:

1. Many motor activities demand that a performer seek *static stability,* that is, remain motionless in one location. To accomplish this, he attempts to use all available sources at his disposal, lower his center of gravity, widen his base of support, and so forth.
2. Other motor activities demand that a performer seek *dynamic stability,* that is, maintain his balance (equilibrium) while constantly changing his body position.

RATIONALE:

Many of our sport activities demand that the performer seek static stability. The wrestler in the down (defense) position does not wish to have his balance destroyed by the up (offensive) wrestler. When weightlifting, the performer must have static stability when moving a heavy weight. In Karate, one desires maximum stability to throw an opponent to the mat.

Most of our motor activities prize stability while the performer is in constant motion, continually moving his base of support. An example might be the actions of a defensive basketball player attempting to stop an opponent from moving to a given position or a wrestler's fending off an attack by an opponent. The skill and grace of a performer on a balance beam illustrate stability while in motion.

ACTIVITIES:

1. A baseball catcher is attempting to tag a runner at home plate. The runner is about to collide with the catcher. Using previous information about stability, list three adjustments the catcher can make to increase his stability prior to collision.
    a.
    b.
    c.

2. A basketball player is guarding an opponent who has the basketball. The defensive player wishes to insure body equilibrium while in constant motion. Three of the following statements indicate methods of realizing this goal. Circle the letter of the statements which depict desired goals.
   a. Take short steps in order to constantly re-establish the base of support.
   b. Make lunging movements to distract the player with the ball.
   c. Stand erect in order to occupy more defensive space.
   d. Lower the center of gravity within the constantly changing base of support.
   e. Keep the center of gravity in the middle of the base of support.

CONCEPT 101: STABILITY

THERE ARE SOME MOTOR ACTIVITIES IN WHICH THE PERFORMER WISHES TO LOSE STABILITY

INFORMATION:

1. In order to lose stability, the center of gravity must fall beyond a margin of the base of support.
2. Stability is lost rapidly when a margin of the base of support is removed.
3. Starting positions in motor skills provide for rapid loss of stability.

RATIONALE:

In motor activities such as track and swimming, a performer who has attained a position emphasizing stability after the "Take your marks!" command wishes to lose that stability at the pistol shot.

During the track start, the athlete raises his hands at the pistol shot, removing the front margin of his base of support. The center of gravity is now in front of his new base of support beneath his feet. The performer immediately becomes unstable in order to begin the race.

While in the preliminary position for the racing start in swimming, the performer has his center of gravity at the extreme front margin of his base of support. Any movement of the legs, trunk, or arms will project the center of gravity beyond the front margin of the base of support. The performer then rapidly loses stability because his center of gravity becomes influenced by the pull of gravity.

ACTIVITIES:

1. The following diagram represents the base of support previous to the pistol shot for a track sprinter.

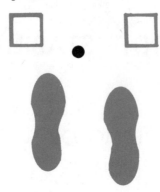

    a. Where is the center of gravity in relation to the base of support?

    b. How is this relationship altered when the pistol fires?

2. The following diagram represents the base of support for a general starting position for motor activities.

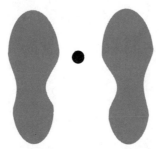

    a. Why is the center of gravity in the middle of the base of support if this factor limits mobility?

    b. What is the rationale for encouraging performers to have their weight on the balls of the feet in such a starting position?

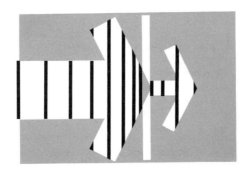

FOLLOW-THROUGH

CONCEPT 102: Follow-through prevents a loss of linear velocity at the moment of impact or release.

CONCEPT 103: Follow-through prevents injuries caused by the abrupt stopping of a moving body part.

CONCEPT 104: Follow-through prevents the violation of certain playing rules.

CONCEPT 105: Follow-through places the body in a "ready position" to begin the next motor activity in a sequence.

CONCEPT 106: Follow-through provides time to perceive feedback information.

CONCEPT 102: FOLLOW-THROUGH

FOLLOW-THROUGH PREVENTS A LOSS OF LINEAR VELOCITY AT THE MOMENT OF IMPACT OR RELEASE

INFORMATION:

1. The principle of summation of forces states that all body levers employed to impart momentum to an object must make their contribution at the moment of impact or instant of release. (See Concept 31.)
2. In many motor skills, objects are either struck by implements attached to the distal end of body levers or are released from the distal end of a body lever.
3. The distal end of a body lever possesses linear velocity. (See Concept 53.)

RATIONALE:

When batting a ball, the bat should achieve maximum linear velocity at the moment of impact with the ball. When throwing a ball, the hand should achieve maximum linear velocity at the instant the ball is released. Note that both the bat and the ball are held at the distal end of the arm, a lever.

If the performer were to allow the velocity of the bat or the hand containing a ball to decrease prior to impact or release, the result would be a weaker hit or a weaker throw.

Follow-through prevents a decrease in linear velocity at the moment of impact of bat on ball or at the instant of release of a thrown ball. By follow-through, the performer maintains a steady contraction of the involved muscles until the motor act is completed.

ACTIVITIES:

1. In the process of throwing a baseball, a player ceases contraction of the triceps before elbow extension is completed. He also releases the ball prior to the completion of wrist flexion.

   a. How do these errors affect the flight of the ball?

   b. Why?

2. A tennis server reduces the force produced by his arm muscles just prior to impact of racquet on ball.

   a. How does this error affect the flight of the ball?

   b. Why?

CONCEPT 103: FOLLOW-THROUGH

FOLLOW-THROUGH PREVENTS INJURIES CAUSED BY THE ABRUPT STOPPING OF A MOVING BODY PART

INFORMATION:

1. A moving body part possesses *momentum*. The abrupt reduction of this momentum may cause injuries to muscles and/or joints.
2. Follow-through permits a gradual deceleration of body levers. The result is a gradual loss of momentum in these levers after impact or release has occurred.

RATIONALE:

When agonist muscles contract, body levers are set in motion, and they generate momentum. An abrupt cessation of the movement in these levers may result in too sudden a stopping of momentum, and injury may occur in the moving body parts.

Follow-through permits a gradual decrease in momentum in these moving body parts.

ACTIVITIES:

1. If horizontal flexion of the glenohumeral joint is actively stopped by contraction of the posterior deltoid before the shot-put leaves the hand, what may occur to the posterior deltoid muscles?

2. If a baserunner attempts to slow down suddenly without sliding into a base, what may occur to his thigh muscles?

CONCEPT 104: FOLLOW-THROUGH

FOLLOW-THROUGH PREVENTS THE VIOLATION OF CERTAIN PLAYING RULES

INFORMATION:

1. Many competitive motor skills are governed by rules which legislate against stepping over certain boundary lines.
2. Follow-through allows for a controlled stopping of total body movement so that stability is re-established before boundary lines are violated.

RATIONALE:

A bowler delivering a ball strides toward a foul line. After release of the ball, if he attempts to stop the movement of all body parts simultaneously, his momentum may cause him to cross the foul line. A violation would result. A similar example could be given for a shot-putter moving across the circle.

Follow-through allows for a gradual diminishing of momentum in the total body or its parts. Time is provided to re-establish a new base of support under the moving center of gravity (see Concept 70). Total body stability is established before the body or one of its parts violates a foul line.

ACTIVITIES:

A free thrower in basketball moves his arms at a linear velocity of 25 feet per second. The weight of the arms plus the basketball is 32 pounds.

a. What is the momentum of the arms?
b. Can the momentum of the arms be transferred to the body? (See Concept 58.)
c. If the movement of the arms is stopped suddenly as the ball is released, how may the body be affected?

d. If the momentum of the arms gradually diminishes during follow-through, what will be the effect on the total body?

e. Was the reduction of momentum in question d caused by a reduction in mass or a reduction in velocity?

CONCEPT 105: FOLLOW-THROUGH

FOLLOW-THROUGH PLACES THE BODY IN A "READY POSITION" TO BEGIN THE NEXT MOTOR ACTIVITY IN A SEQUENCE

INFORMATION:

1. A tennis player who serves the ball and then enters the court in a "ready position" is prepared to field a serve returned by his opponent. A tumbler proceeds through his routine, executing a series of specific stunts, and follows-through with the next successive stunt in mind.
2. Stability may be lacking at the end of one movement and must be regained in order to perform the next movement in a sequence.
3. Follow-through at the end of one movement permits the re-establishment of stability and places the body in a position to begin the next movement in the sequence.

RATIONALE:

A tennis server must insure proper contact with the ball and then must move rapidly onto the court to contest the point if the serve is returned. In order to accomplish the sequence of movements, he must reestablish stability after the serve is completed and is then in a ready position to move onto the court.

Should the server be off balance at the completion of the serve, he would experience difficulty in moving onto the court.

Follow-through at the end of the serve provides time to control body momentum, re-establish stability, and use momentum gathered during the serve to move the body onto the court.

ACTIVITIES:

1. A baseball pitcher releases the ball and then must field a batted ball hit down the first base line.
   a. Does this sequence of movements involve a change of direction for the pitcher's body?

b. If the pitcher ceased all movement as soon as the ball was released, what would be the effect upon stability?

c. How does follow-through benefit the pitcher in changing direction after the ball is released?

2. A free thrower in basketball must be prepared to move for the rebound if a shot is unsuccessful.
   a. If the free thrower ceased all movement as soon as the ball was released, what would be the effect on stability?

   b. How does follow-through help to place him in a ready position to move in for a rebound?

CONCEPT 106: FOLLOW-THROUGH

FOLLOW-THROUGH PROVIDES TIME TO PERCEIVE FEEDBACK INFORMATION

INFORMATION:

1. Through the body's many receptors, input concerning a given performance is fed back to the individual. This information (data) is used to aid him in improving his next attempt at a motor skill.
2. *Feedback* permits the athlete to analyze his performance and to make corrections so that errors are not repeated.

RATIONALE:

At the completion of certain motor skills, follow-through provides a brief inactive period during which visual or kinesthetic feedback can be received and interpreted by the performer.

A tennis player whose initial serve is unsuccessful uses the brief interval during his follow-through to analyze the imperfect performance and to identify possible solutions.

A skillful free thrower in basketball knows, almost as soon as the ball leaves his hand, if his attempt will be successful. During the period of follow-through, while the ball is travelling toward the goal, the player is provided with a brief interval to analyze his performance and identify possible errors.

ACTIVITIES:

1. Circle the letter of the activities which would present a period of follow-through during which an athlete could receive feedback and analyze his performance.
    a. A front somersault during a tumbling routine
    b. A baseball pitch at which the batter did not swing
    c. Missing the first of two free throws in basketball
    d. A golf drive from the tee
    e. A missed field goal in football
    f. A left hand punch in a boxing match
    g. A jump shot in basketball
    h. Shooting an arrow in archery

2. A place kicker in football is instructed to keep his head down for a short period after the ball is kicked. Since he cannot see the ball in flight, what sense receptors provide him with feedback?

3. During the follow-through at the end of the delivery of a bowling ball, what analysis might be running through the mind of the bowler?

GLOSSARY

Acceleration: The rate of change of velocity.

Action potential: A marked change in the electrical state of the cell.

Adaptation of stress: A phenomenon whereby one misaligned body segment forces adjacent segments out of alignment.

Aerobic exercises: Those which require the consumption of oxygen.

Agonist: A prime mover; a muscle which produces most of the force in order to move a bone.

Anaerobic metabolism: The production of cellular energy in which chemicals other than oxygen are consumed.

Anatomical position: One in which the individual assumes the position of military attention with the palms of the hands facing forward.

Angle of pull of muscle: The angle formed between the line of pull of a contracting muscle and the plane of the bone which is moved.

Angle of takeoff: The angle formed between the line of flight of an object and the surface from which that object departs.

Angular motion: The movement occurring when an object rotates around an axis which is within the mass of that object.

Angular velocity: The rate at which an object travels in an angular path.

Antagonist: A muscle whose action opposes the motion occurring at a joint.

Assistant mover: A muscle which aids a prime mover in overcoming a great resistance.

Axis of motion: A fulcrum; a fixed point about which angular motion occurs.

Base of support: The points in contact with the supporting surfaces and the two dimensional area between those points of contact.

Bipennate: The converging of fascicles to both sides of a central tendon like the plumes of a feather.

Cardinal plane: Any plane which divides the body into two equally sized portions.

Center of gravity: A point about which all parts of the body will balance. A hypothetical point in the body where all of the weight of the body is centered.

Centrifugal force: A special application of the law of inertia; the force which seemingly attempts to pull an object out of its orbit.

Centripetal force: The force which attempts to maintain an object in an orbital path.

Coefficient of friction: A ratio of the force needed to start or stop an object in motion and the force holding the object against the surface.

Concentric contraction: The contraction of a muscle as it shortens from its resting length.

Curvilinear motion: Movement occurring when an object follows a curved path or an orbit around an external axis.

Cutaneous receptor: Sensory bodies in the skin which are stimulated by changes in the external environment.

Dark muscle fiber: Skeletal muscle fibers containing greater amounts of myoglobin which are capable of sustaining contractions over longer periods of time.

Distal: A part which is further from the body center.

Dynamic stability: The state of possessing equilibrium while in motion.

Eccentric contraction: The gradual lengthening against resistance of a concentrically contracted muscle.

Eccentric thrust: A force passing through an object at some point other than its center of gravity.

Efficiency: The ratio of work output over work input.

Exteroceptive reflex: An automatic act triggered by stimuli from the external environment.

Fascicle: A collection of individual muscle fibers (cells) bounded by a tight, dense covering of connective tissue.

Feedback: Knowledge of results of a performance.

First-class lever: A simple machine which has its fulcrum at some intermediate location between its resistance point and its force point.

Foot-pound: The amount of work accomplished when one pound of resistance is moved a distance of one foot.

Force: A push or pull exerted against a resistance.

Force arm: In a lever system, the linear distance from the force point to the axis of motion (fulcrum).

Force point: The point on a lever where a force is exerted in an attempt to move the lever.

Friction: The resistance to motion created by a contact between two surfaces.

Frontal plane: An imaginary surface passing through the body from side to side dividing the body into anterior and posterior portions.

Fulcrum: The axis of motion (rotation) in a lever system.

Fusiform muscle: The parallel arrangement of fascicles with the longitudinal axis of the muscle, finishing at both ends in tendons.

Glycolytic sequence: A complex series of chemical reactions which systematically dissolve sugar molecules.

Helping synergists: Muscles which cancel out one another's undesired movement, thus allowing one another's desired movement to occur.

Horizontal plane: An imaginary surface passing through the body, parallel to the floor and dividing the body into superior and inferior portions.

Inertia: The tendency of an object to remain at rest or in uniform motion in a straight line.

Isometric contraction: A contraction in which a muscle retains its length, but increases its tension.

Isotonic contraction: A contraction in which a muscle fiber shortens.

Kinesthesis: The perception of muscle movement and the relative alignment of the performer's body parts in space.

Lever: A bony segment which moves around an axis of motion (fulcrum).

Linear velocity: The rate at which an object travels in a translatory (linear) path.

Line of muscle pull: A line that lies between the attachments of a muscle.

Locomotion: Movement occurring when the human body provides the force necessary to produce motion.

Mass: The result of dividing the weight of an object by a constant number (at sea level, 32) representing the force of gravity.

Mechanical advantage: A ratio of the amount of resistance overcome compared to the amount of energy expended.

Mid position: A position of the hands in which the palms face one another.

Mobility: The state of being capable of movement.

Moment of force: The product of the amount of force applied to a lever multiplied by the perpendicular distance from the force point to the distal end of the lever.

Moment of inertia: The product of the amount of resistance overcome, multiplied by the perpendicular distance from the distal end of the lever, to the axis of motion (fulcrum).

Momentum: The product of the mass of an object multiplied by its velocity.

Motion: A change of position.

Multipennate: The converging of fascicles to many central tendons, as in the deltoideus muscle.

Muscle spindle: A proprioceptor, a sensor for the kinesthetic sense which is stimulated when skeletal muscle is stretched.

Myoglobin: Muscle hemoglobin; a protein compound capable of combining chemically with oxygen.

Nonrotatory component: The portion of a force or a resistance which does not produce movement at an axis of motion (joint).

Oxidative process: A complex series of chemical reactions in which electrons are "freed" from the foodstuffs we take into our bodies.

Pale muscle fiber: Skeletal muscle fibers with minimal myoglobin but capable of producing rapid contractions against lesser resistances.

Pectoral girdle: An anatomical unit consisting of the clavicle, scapula, and the humerus.

Pelvic girdle: An anatomical unit consisting of the left and right innominate bones (ilium, ischium, pubis) and the sacrum.

Pennate muscle: The converging of fascicles to one side of a tendon running logitudinally throughout the muscle.

Perception: The process of receiving and interpreting external and internal stimuli.

Periphery: The external margin of an object or an area.

Perpendicular: At a right angle to.

Physiological advantage: The physiological ability of a muscle to contract. Muscles are at their greatest physiological advantage when at or stretched slightly beyond the resting length.

Plane: A level and flat surface which is often imaginary.

Points of contact: The parts of the body (or object) which are in contact with the supporting surface.

Prime mover: An agonist, a muscle which produces most of the force which moves a bone.

Pronated hands: A position in which the palms face rearward in the anatomical position.

Prone: A body position in which the face is down.

Proprioceptive reflex: Movement triggered by a special receptor sensitive to changes in body position.

Proprioceptors: Receptors which are stimulated by changes in body position or the alignment of body parts.

Proximal: A body part which is closer to the body center.

Rectilinear motion: Movement occurring when an object follows a straight line.

Resistance: An opposing force to be overcome.

Resistance arm: In a lever system, the linear distance from the resistance point to the axis of motion (fulcrum).

Resistance point: The center of gravity of the moving portion of the body lever.

Resting length: The length of a muscle when that muscle's body segment is in the anatomical position.

Rotation: Angular movement, motion around a fixed axis of motion.

Rotatory component: The portion of a force or a resistance which produces movement at an axis of motion (fulcrum).

Sagittal plane: An imaginary surface passing through the body from front to back, dividing the body into left and right portions.

Second-class lever: A simple machine which has its resistance point at some intermediate position between its fulcrum and its force point.

Shunt muscle: Has its upper attachment nearer the joint upon which it acts than is true of its lower attachment. Most of its force is nonrotarory and stabilizes the joint spanned.

Sliding friction: The resistance to motion created by contact between two surfaces which are free to slide.

Spurt muscle: Has its lower attachments nearer the joint upon which it acts than is true of its upper attachment. Most of its force is rotary and produces motion.

Stability: Possessing equilibrium, the ability to resist a force which could cause motion.

Stabilizer: A muscle which fixes one bony segment so that movement can occur in a bone articulating at that segment.

Starting friction: The resistance to motion created by the contact between two surfaces; must be overcome before one of the surfaces can move.

Static stability: The ability to resist a force that could set an object in motion.

Stretch reflexes: An automatic contracting of a skeletal muscle that has become stretched; a postural reflex.

Supinated hands: A position in which the palms face forward in the anatomical position.

Supine: A position in which the body is lying in a face-up position.

Taut: The condition of being tightly drawn.

Third-class lever: A simple machine having its force point at some intermediate position between its resistance point and its fulcrum.

Torque: A twist exerted around an axis of motion.

Translatory motion: Movement in which an object follows (1) a straight path or (2) a circular path, sometimes around an external axis of motion.

True force arm: The perpendicular distance from the line of pull of a muscle to the axis of motion.

True resistance arm: The perpendicular distance from the line of pull of a resistance to the axis of motion.

True synergist: A muscle whose contraction cancels out the nondesired movement of a prime mover (agonist).

Unipennate: See pennate muscle.

Velocity: The rate of change of motion.

Visual cues: Perceived visual stimuli which contribute to equilibrium and/or performance.

Work: The process of exerting a force which moves a resistance through a distance. Heat is a by-product of work.